The
Dark
City

# The Dark City

*A True Account
of Adventures of a
Secret Agent in Berlin*

*as told to*

# Hartvig Andersen

*Rinehart & Company, Inc.
New York          Toronto*

Published simultaneously in Canada by
Clarke, Irwin & Company, Ltd., Toronto

Copyright, 1954, by Rinehart & Company, Inc.
Printed in the United States of America
Library of Congress Catalog Card Number: 54-5397

The
Dark
City

# chapter one

The big truck poked its broad nose out of the damp fog—a lead-gray, jointed monster, whose bulk and noise seemed to fill the entire narrow street in the little Danish provincial town of Kolding on this cold dreary afternoon, the first of February, 1945.

With a deep vibrating roar that suggested a great resource of latent, eager power, it climbed the steep grade towards the top of the hill, where I had spent the last ten minutes trying to pass away the time as inconspicuously as possible, alternately studying the uninspiring window displays of a radio dealer, a bicycle shop and a grocer's store.

I stole a glance at my watch. The dial showed five-thirty P.M. He was on time. I gathered my coat around me and dug my hands deep down in my pockets. Their firm pressure against my thighs gave me a comfortable feeling of reassurance. The last couple of hours had been so packed with frantic brain work and desperate ideas that I had almost forgotten the existence of my own solid and serviceable limbs.

3

Without moving away from the empty cardboard trappings of the grocer's window, I turned my head slightly to watch the progress of the truck, laboring up the hill with a hard sound like small hammers beating on resounding metal. It was a large, heavy vehicle with a trailer attached. Moisture coursed in small dirty streams down the gray metal body that might easily have been mistaken for a local thickening of the fog. The words "FISH EXPORT" were painted in heavy black letters along the side, and underneath in smaller lettering the name of a firm. A quick glance at the license plates told me this was it.

I turned away from the window, strolled casually to the curb and put one hand in the air—an ordinary man in a nice, dark overcoat and a soft brown hat, a traveler hitching a ride, a commonplace daily occurrence in a German-occupied country where transport facilities had been reduced to a minimum.

The big truck came to a dead stop.

"Got room for another fish?" I asked through the half-open window of the cab. That was the password I had been given. I felt a little embarrassed saying it.

"Get in!" answered a curt voice.

Clumsily I climbed up on the running board and into the semi-dark cabin where I practically collapsed on the seat. The leather band inside my hat felt soaking wet.

The driver peered searchingly through the side windows, as he picked up speed. The humming of the engine was soothing.

"Did they bother you?"

"The porter from the hotel stopped me out in the square and told me there were two men waiting at the hotel. They had asked for me and he was quite sure they were informers working for the Germans. He advised me to get going as quickly as possible."

The driver lit a cigarette, letting the truck run itself for a moment. He inhaled the smoke greedily. The skin on his narrow angular jaw tightened.

4

"And I suppose you were crazy enough to go back to the hotel?" His tone suggested no great confidence in my ability to cope with a critical situation.

"No, I beat it down the nearest side street. I left my bag at the hotel and didn't dare go back for it. I wandered round for two hours looking at windows. It's damned difficult to hide away in a small town like this. You get the feeling that somebody's watching you the whole time."

The panic of the last few hours, the fear of watchful eyes and two sinister men appearing at any moment to close in on me from each end of a narrow alley, welled up in me once more. I tried to shake it off.

"What was in the bag?" the driver asked sharply. His voice revealed no nervousness—only cool-headed reflection.

"Pajamas, toilet things and a book by a chap called Boccaccio. I usually read him to fall asleep."

"Any name on the book?"

"Just the author's—Boccaccio."

The driver let the wheel spin through his long slender fingers as he negotiated a bend in the road. They were surprisingly well-formed hands. I glanced at his face, but his expression told me nothing. His eyes were rigidly fixed on the road, but the cigarette in the right corner of his mouth jumped violently up and down. Somehow or other it gave me the impression that he was having an argument with himself—whether this after all was worth the trouble, and whether he dared run the risks involved. I clenched my fists inside my pockets. Should half a year of preparation and intensive training, the entire carefully calculated and well-planned scheme, suddenly break down, because some Danish truck driver got cold feet?

Like a man who is drowning, everything came back to me in sharp flashes—all the struggles, the dangers, despairs and hopes. First, the whole underground fight in Denmark against the Nazis. The monotonous and at the same time nerve-racking daily life in an occupied country. An ordinary, innocent job in the daytime and school at night—a tough, adult school where the main subjects were sabotage, explosives and weapons.

I came to know the excitement of the chase and discovered that it has its drawbacks when you, yourself, become the quarry. It got so that I would start nervously when the telephone rang or when there was a knock on the door. It seemed as if I developed new senses, the senses of the hunted that feel the danger just before it is there. I learned discipline, teamwork and responsibility—and a great deal about other people's self-sacrifice and devotion to duty.

And then one day, without warning, catastrophe thundered down on our fragile defenses. The Germans broke up the group to which I belonged. Some of the members were thrown in prison, others were shot. My father was taken to a jail in Germany and my brother to a concentration camp. I managed to escape to Sweden.

Now as I sat looking through the windshield, watching the dark, wet road like an endless ribbon beneath the wheels of the huge truck, I understood that without all that experience I would have been no good for the job I had just set out to do.

But my story did not really begin until the day on which I, as a refugee in Stockholm, contacted certain high-ranking members of the Office of Strategic Services. This happened in the early autumn of 1944. One of the objectives of the O.S.S. at that time was to train and smuggle into Berlin, if possible, agents who could send out intelligence reports through one of several courier and radio-communication systems. Also they were anxious to organize there a group who could sabotage various strategic objectives.

I felt sure I could help the O.S.S. in the training of these agents because, though I had been born in Denmark, I had spent my childhood in Riga and lived for several years in Germany before the war. I knew the country in and out, spoke fluent German and understood some Russian. For a couple of months I did my best to give them all the good tips I could think of, to help them carry out their mission and come back alive. Then off they went! Some of them kept in touch with us, but not for long. Others we never heard from. Gradually a decision was forming in my mind, and one day I went to see my chief in his office.

"The next one you send off had better be me," I said.

He leaned back in his chair and placed his finger tips together. He didn't seem particularly surprised. On the contrary, I had a feeling that he had been waiting a long time to hear those words.

"Why do you want to go?"

I could have given him several reasons. I felt that I owed so much to so many. My father and brother, my comrades in Denmark, and he himself sitting there before me—a man who had done so much for me, and who had become my friend. And all those whom he represented, fellows at the front all over the world, fellows I had never seen, but who risked their lives so that I would be able to return home one day, without having to sneak along close to the walls or dart from one hide-out to the other.

"I guess it would be the most sensible thing if I went myself. I've got better chances of pulling it off than anyone we've sent down there so far." I paused a moment. "And even if I realize this has nothing to do with it—you know I have several good reasons of my own."

The chief jumped up from his chair. "Okay. It might be an idea at that! Wonder why I didn't think of it myself," he said with a wink. "I'll have to discuss it with some others. I suppose you're ready to start training right away?"

He was on the telephone even before I got out the door.

The day after my talk with the chief in Stockholm I started the most rigorous training. I brushed up my knowledge of sabotage technique, marveling at the progress that had been made in the past six months. I was taught the most vulnerable points of a seemingly insensitive mechanism like a locomotive. I was introduced to a variety of subjects—from photographing documents and the use of codes for writing reports to opening safes and the best method for killing an enemy without leaving any trace.

I had very little spare time, but when I had an hour or two there was always the BOOK—a manual on sabotage, printed in eight languages with different-colored pages for each language. Its contents were far removed from its slightly boudoir-like appearance. It was the secret agent's and saboteur's A B C. It contained a great many useful paragraphs which, used the right way, could facilitate everyday proceedings in many respects. I was particularly fascinated by the chapter on hand-to-hand fighting because it gave a detailed description of how to kill a man with a certain chop of the hand across his neck. Unfortunately I never got the chance to practice this magical little blow, because I could never find anyone willing to furnish me with a neck for the good of the cause. But the book described many other interesting methods. We nicknamed it "How to kill a man without noise in six easy lessons."

But I had more faith in the old, tried and true methods of effective self-defense. The man who taught me the use of all the different firearms I might come across was the famous Norwegian saboteur-ace, Max Manus, who at that time was taking one of his numerous involuntary "vacations" in Sweden. One miserable autumn morning we traveled by train to the Norwegian volunteers' camp outside Stockholm, he dressed in skiing clothes with an enormous rucksack full of weapons and ammunition over his shoulder, I in my usual battle outfit—winter coat and soft hat. Our firing range was a typical Swedish landscape with rocks and great firs that filled the morning air with their keen, fresh smell. Outside the range there were little fields with millions of stones and a top soil so thin that you had a feeling that if you started removing the stones, the entire field would disappear.

8

We aimed at unflinching German soldiers cut out in cardboard. Max Manus cursed, lying face down on the stones and lining the Germans up in his sights.

"I just can't get used to them," he complained and plonked around into one of the cardboard Germans. "In England we used to fire at Japs. It's a damned nuisance—all these different sizes of fascists. You have to revise your whole system of aiming. It's like learning a new language."

Max was like a man gone haywire in a shooting gallery. Only when his fingers were raw with pressing the trigger did I get a chance. We killed off the equivalent of an entire division, and I learned a great deal. I learned how to shoot from the hip, an accomplishment I had always envied the heroes of the Wild West. Max and I became great friends there on our own private little front, although we never talked anything but shooting. He had been in the game too long himself to start asking questions. We expressed our mutual esteem through the hard, unfeeling medium of technical arsenal language. He was a small and very ordinary man to look at. His anonymous face was a disguise in itself. But he had a will of inflexible steel.

Finally I got my orders and was told to learn them by heart to avoid carrying notes. At the same time, I was set to work what concealed itself under the totally misleading name of IN-NOCENT TEXT LETTERS. This turned out to be a cipher, by means of which one could smuggle secret information into personal or business letters, using a prearranged key word. Innocent text letters are an unbreakable code, unless you happen to know the keyword. To me they presented a special difficulty, because they demanded unfailingly accurate spelling. And as my spelling, in any of the languages I knew, happened to be terrible, I made up my mind, while struggling with the cipher book, that INNOCENT TEXT LETTERS would be the very last means by which I would send my reports to London.

A little shriveled-up American woman, whose outward appearance of asceticism disguised a rare knowledge of cognac

9

and other noble spirits, taught me micro-photography. Finally I was inoculated and maltreated to ward off all manner of diseases, pumped so full of poison that I lay mortally ill for eight days thereafter. What a normal, healthy constitution can build up in the course of thirty-two years can nowadays be completely destroyed in a few hours by the skilled modern physician. I take off my hat to doctors and the high standards of medical science, but I prefer my own patent medicine— a glass of strong, warming liquor.

When I was fully recovered from my bad reaction to the inoculations, I made final preparations for departure. My chief gave me last-minute instructions. His final words were: "You realize there is now a chance that the Russians might reach Berlin first, although that is not the plan at present. If this should happen and you have difficulties in making your position understood, make every effort to talk with an intelligence officer. Report to him that you have had to use a false name and passport and that you are an American. Then tell him you are really me and give him my name. Also use your passwords. Insist that he notify SHAEF immediately so we can put the machinery to work at once to extricate you. But only do this as a last resort." Then he added with well-controlled emotion, "You know you can count on me to do everything possible for you. We are all wishing you the best luck in the world."

I then departed alone by train for Gothenburg where I was met by contacts as prearranged. The next day I boarded the small boat that was to take me, an O.S.S. secret agent, and my suitcase on my first lap from Sweden to Denmark.

The fishing smack was working for the underground. It was registered in a Swedish harbor, but its secret mission was to carry weapons halfway across to Denmark, where it would contact a similar Danish boat that took them the rest of the way.

We had to wait two weeks before we met the Danish boat, and during those fourteen days we fished, partly because it gave us an authentic appearance and partly because we enjoyed it. My four companions on board were also of the resistance movement. We were a little world of our own, hard, primitive. On the deck we waded around in fish. Below in a secret compartment which could only be found if experts started measuring up the boat, we waded knee-deep in weapons. Our main asset was a 250-horsepower twin-cylinder Bolinder engine that gave us a maximum speed of 14 to 15 knots. This meant that in most situations we could make a fast getaway from the German boats and reach safety in Swedish territorial waters. But should we get in a tight spot, we had machine guns and bombs that could easily sink the light German speedboats.

It was a fisherman's life. Bending over the greasy naval charts in our small, foul-smelling steering cabin, the skipper piloted us like a Nordic Ulysses in and out between the skerries on the Swedish coasts, when we ran into some harbor to unload our catch.

And it was also a life of luxury. In the evenings, when we clattered down into the cabin, weary and dirty, dressed in oil-stained dungarees, leather caps that covered the ears, enormous sweaters with choker collars and lead-heavy woolen underpants, we were greeted by the daintiest virginal bunks with sheets of the finest linen and costly pale-blue quilted eiderdowns, cool and smooth as a young girl's skin. As a rule we had enough *savoir vivre* to take off our heavy, wet seaboots before pulling the silk eiderdowns up to our unshaven cheeks.

But at last the day came when we contacted the Danish boat. Eager hands grabbed my luggage—a small bag, or kit, with a few personal belongings, and a fiber suitcase for my "work"—and as I swung a leg over the railing of the Danish vessel I was greeted by a group of laughing, bearded faces exactly like the ones I was leaving behind.

After landing, it took eight days of being smuggled through my own country before I reached Kolding where I was picked up by the truck.

The driver sitting beside me finished his cigarette and mashed out the butt in the ashtray on the dashboard. Then he took a firm grip on the wheel as if to indicate that he had made up his mind.

"Now get this. I don't like the part with the two squealers. It doubles the risk. I'm playing your game, otherwise you wouldn't be here, but I'm playing it my way. I got orders to slip you across the border to Germany, and that's okay. But they forgot to tell me we might be chased by the Gestapo. When I leave you in Hamburg, you're through worrying about the two informers waiting at the hotel. But me, I have to come back here."

He paused as if to give his words added weight. I shrugged my shoulders in resignation.

Suddenly he turned towards me with a wide grin, took one hand off the wheel and gave me a hearty slap on the back.

"Cheer up! A fellow can think aloud, can't he? I respect the work you're trying to do, even if I don't know the first thing about it. Hide and seek with the Gestapo in their own back yard! Christ Almighty! Not for me!" He edged towards the door, as if he were making room for me in some niche in the Hall of Fame. He continued: "And as the chances of getting to be a hero are better than usual on this trip, I suggest you help to build up my accident policy with one of those pretty five-hundred-crown notes. Is that a deal?" He looked at me eagerly.

I was greatly amused at this well-balanced mixture of business sense and patriotism. At the same time I heaved a sigh of relief. Was that all? I dug down in my breast pocket and pulled out my notecase. I opened it and started counting out the notes.

"I think I can just make it," I said and feigned a worried look as I counted the notes once more. There was no reason to encourage a further display of his business talents. "You'll get the money, when we part in Hamburg."

He seemed satisfied. "In a few minutes we'll pull up at the place of contact in Aabenraa. I'll see if there is any mail for you or change of orders. From there we go straight to the border."

"How do you plan to get me across?" I asked.

"Just leave that to me," he said casually, as if I had really been changed into a crate of fish—possibly not even one of the better grades.

"By the way, my name's Hansen. Evald to my friends." He put out his hand, and I took it, once more wondering about his long, supple fingers. This was certainly not the big, rough fellow I had expected to see as the driver of a fish truck.

"Schmidt!" I replied. "Aage Schmidt!" I tried to put as much honest conviction into a false name as I could. I had been practicing for months in Stockholm, and I noted with pleasure that the name sounded quite familiar by now.

"I get it. Schmidt! What's in a name, anyway? One's as good as the other," said Evald with a shrewd grin which let me understand that he too might have other names between friends.

I was glad that the weather was foggy. It gave me a feeling of safety, a feeling of being well hidden. Even so I tensed my toes inside my shoes every time we were overtaken by another car, and I didn't relax until it disappeared over some hilltop ahead of us.

I continued these toe exercises, until all of a sudden I felt very stupid. The danger might well come at us from the other direction. Defiantly I straightened out my toes. If I were going to see pursuers in every automobile or behind every tree along the road, I might as well give up right away.

An irregular pattern of small light beams from windows with faulty black-out arrangements told me that we had reached Aabenraa, the last Danish town before the German border. There was hardly anyone in the streets. Here, as in every other Danish town, it seemed as if life ceased abruptly as soon as darkness came. Evenings and nights belonged to the Germans.

13

We passed a German military patrol, motor vehicles with undimmed lights. The beams cut through the windshield and flooded the cab. For a moment I had a feeling of standing stark naked on a brightly lit stage. But the patrol ignored us and passed on. A Danish fish truck, bound for Hamburg, was the most common spectacle of the border traffic.

Evald pulled up somewhere in the outskirts of the town. He jumped down from the truck and disappeared into the darkness. I hoped and prayed that he would bring back some mail for me. There was a sour smell of sweat, damp clothes and oil in the cabin. Had I been a smoker, I would have lighted a cigarette. Instead I rolled down the side window. The night air tasted raw and wet.

Suddenly there was a tear in the darkness. A door was opened and for a brief moment light poured from the cosy, bright entrance of a house, a few yards back from the road. I saw the silhouettes of two men who shook hands, whereupon one of them bent down and lifted something. A voice called through the darkness: "Good trip—and good luck!"

Those parting words did much to cheer me up. They were probably the last I would hear from my friends for many months. I found something symbolic in the fact that the words came from a man I had never seen and probably never would see—one of the many nameless soldiers in the Danish underground army who at the peril of his own life had helped transport me and my luggage this far.

The unknown voice in the darkness gave me a feeling that I was not alone but one of many.

I could not understand why Evald was so long coming back, but at last he opened the door and climbed into the driver's seat. I looked at him in surprise and anxiety.

"I thought you would have a suitcase for me? Wasn't it there?" I was referring to the suitcase containing the articles for my work. It had been sent on ahead of me when I reached

14

Denmark. My personal kit I had left behind, in a hurry, in Kolding.

He started up the engine and swung out into the road.

"Couldn't be bothered to drag it all the way up here," he said casually. "It was easier to dump it in your luxury suite at the back. You'll find it in an hour or so, when you have to be tucked in for the night."

The suitcase was the last thing I had packed before leaving Stockholm. It was filled to the brim with bottles of cognac and cigarettes, together with coffee, some of the few remaining negotiable commodities in Germany or German-occupied territory. I had hopes that they would help me along on my first difficult lap to Berlin.

The huge highway schooner continued steadily south mile after mile. In the glow of the dim lights the country loomed vast and desolate.

I had a nasty feeling that ours was the only vehicle moving in the border territory that night and therefore must appear twice as suspicious. I looked at my watch.

"Shouldn't we be getting close now?" I tried to make my voice sound as if my question arose through boredom.

Evald peered into the darkness to fix our position.

"No rush, another quarter of an hour to go. But I can understand your getting jumpy. We'll get it all straight now. It isn't difficult to understand the setup. Just before the border there's a place where all the fish trucks pull in to check their engines before the next stretch. I'll park the truck there and bundle you into the back as quick as a wink. I have a place for you among the fish crates. Standing room only."

He made a deprecating gesture with his hand, as a host who would have liked to do more for his guests.

"What I said about a luxury suite was maybe a bit exaggerated. In fact, you're going to have a tough hour in there, but it's the only way that's almost foolproof."

"What do you mean—foolproof?" I asked. That was all I wanted to know. It would be all right if he laid me on ice in one of the fish crates, as long as it meant safety. Already I could see myself standing hidden among the tall pile of crates which efficient German policemen removed one by one, until I finally stood there, hands in the air and eyes blinking in the mercilessly probing beam of a flashlight.

"What happens if they start searching the truck?" I asked, continuing my thoughts aloud.

Evald laughed. "Search? I know the guys on duty tonight. We're pals. I have my own way of keeping them happy."

Shortly afterwards we coasted down the hill towards the border post at Krusaa. The Germans hadn't bothered to black out the post. The barriers were fully lit and a cold, white light glared from the rooms of the building. After the long trip in total darkness, it was like being in a floodlit arena. Shrill voices, laughter and the roar of a radio turned on full volume, accentuated the impression of a low-class place of amusement going full pitch. So this was the German version of the Danish border! The spectacle was both humiliating and glaringly boastful.

Evald pulled the truck over to the left side of the road, a few hundred yards in front of the barriers, and parked it by a stone fence, surrounding an area planted with trees, which in the darkness looked like a large park. Ahead of us there was another fish truck standing with its headlights turned off. Its driver had probably gone off somewhere to get a beer.

My respect for Evald's cunning increased. Hiding me away here, right under the noses of the Germans, was such a daring idea that even the craftiest Gestapo bloodhounds wouldn't think of it. This was the one spot on the whole route where we were least likely to be disturbed, and even if anything unexpected should happen, there was an excellent possibility for instant flight through the dense trees and shrubbery on our left.

Evald opened the door and stepped down from the truck without hurrying.

"When you hear me whistle, jump down on the stone fence and run round to the back of the bogie. Take it easy. No German here would dream of looking for you."

There was not the slightest trace of worry in his voice. He spoke briefly and to the point.

I heard him open the front hood and close it again. I could hear him from my seat in the cab, as he walked alongside the trailer, kicking the tires to see if they needed air. Then I couldn't hear him any more. For a short while nothing happened. The emptiness was filled by the deafening racket from the border post. I waited tensely gripping the handle of the half-open door. Suddenly I heard a low whistling outside, a few bars from a popular tune.

I rushed out of the door. The stones were wet and slippery, and in my eagerness I could barely keep myself from falling. In next to no time I had covered the distance to the back of the truck. Evald had drawn the heavy bolts from the two metal plates that served as doors. He bent down and made a kind of stirrup with his hands; I placed my foot in it and pulled myself up by the metal plates. I moved sideways into the compartment until my progress was obstructed by a hard object that wouldn't budge. There was so little room in which to move around that I had to put one foot on an obstruction which turned out to be my suitcase.

"The Jerries haven't opened this door yet," Evald whispered, while he got the bolts ready. "They always open the side door—it's easier than getting in here between the truck and the trailer. Don't forget to duck, when they flash their lights inside!"

Then the metal plates clanged shut, the bolts were shot into place, and I was alone in the darkness.

Balancing on one leg with the other resting on my case, my back against the steel doors and my nose pressed against a pile of crates, I would have looked pretty grotesque to anyone who opened the doors by mistake.

But my mind wasn't occupied with such thoughts at the

moment. I had an oblong space the size of a stack of fish crates to move about in, and it was only through cunning adaptation of several yoga-like movements that I succeeded in edging around sufficiently to rest on both feet. This gave me freedom of movement so that I could bend my knees at a critical moment, without the risk of a noisy collision with the suitcase.

I passed a hand over the rough, damp fish crates to find out how high they were stacked. I started violently when I suddenly felt something cold and slimy in my fingers. Then I remembered where I was, and overcame the intense feeling of revulsion. I could feel the fish like dead cold lumps between the bars. Before long my fingers were cold and insensitive.

The fish were packed in layers of ice which filled the compartment with a raw, wet cold, so dense that I could almost taste it—a taste of salt and seaweed, as if I were standing on the bottom of a deep and dark ocean with my mouth full of salt water.

Gradually I discovered that it was not completely dark inside. A phosphorescent glow lingered over the crates, the palest shade of greenish white. Fascinated I stared at this weird, ghostly light, feeling rather uneasy, until I realized that it came from the dead fish.

I stood erect in my narrow coffin, while a thousand thoughts flew through my head. What if I should cough or sneeze at the critical moment, or what if some cramped muscle compelled me to change my position? Or what if the Germans, contrary to all predictions, preferred to open my door that night?

Unconsciously I started discriminating between the sounds that came from the outside and those that came from inside the compartment. I noticed a faint, barely audible scratching sound, little creepy crawly noises coming from somewhere inside. Inadvertently I pressed my back closer to the steel plates, moving a few inches away from the living darkness before me. I felt that I was treading on something soft and resilient, something that kept weaving in and out around my legs. I tried to kick it away, but it stuck to my foot. I felt as if small slimy creatures were moving up my legs. I could not think of any reasonable explanation. What was at large in the compartment?

"Pull yourself together! You're just suffering from claustrophobia," I told myself. Presently the truck started up, and I found I had other things to think of.

We had barely started moving, before we stopped again. The voices and the laughter I had heard at a distance were now right outside. I heard the radio roaring out a tune, and the words stuck in my mind although I didn't listen to their meaning: "*Am Rhein hab' ich ein Madel kennengelernt* (I met a girl at the Rhine)." There was a sound of heavy footsteps alongside the truck, and three or four German voices shouted something all at the same time. The footsteps died away, and from somewhere farther ahead I could hear Evald's cocky voice. He said something which made the Germans roar with laughter. Judging by the volume of sound, they must have been standing near the driver's cab.

A long time passed—or maybe it was only a moment—I had no way of telling. The man who knew the girl on the Rhine kept on telling the world about her over the radio. Now and then there was a new burst of laughter. A German shouted something to one of his comrades who answered, as far as I could hear, from inside the building.

"Get it over, get it over, get it over." The words throbbed in my temples in time with the tune from the loud-speaker—but it wasn't the man and his Rhine maiden I was thinking of, as I listened with my ear strained against the steel plates.

There was a sound of rattling metal from the building. More footsteps and voices coming closer. Suddenly someone started working on the bolts of the side door. Quick as lightning I doubled up my knees. A moment later the door was opened. A faint light from outside penetrated the compartment. I could see the bars of the crates beside me. I clenched my fist round one of them to support myself in my crouching position.

"And what do you think she said, when I was through with her?" That was Evald's voice right outside. He made a dramatic pause. "Well, she said, 'Nothing happened, did it?' 'Happened?' I said. 'What the hell kind of a guy does that make me, when you haven't even felt anything!'"

The Germans outside sniggered. I heard heavy, nail-studded boots scraping against metal and felt a slight shaking in the truck. In the beam of the flashlight the contours of the fish crates stood out clearly. I ducked even lower and forced my head down upon my chest. The contours of the crates faded again, came back for a moment and finally disappeared almost completely.

"Well, what are you trying to slip across tonight, you old smuggler?" said the German in the doorway. His heavy boot kicked against one of the crates resounding hollowly through the compartment.

"Take a look for yourself," replied Evald. Now he spoke his own mixture of German and Danish, painful to the sensitive ear of an accomplished linguist, but practical and effective. "But you will have to lug a hundred crates of fish out of there first!"

"You be careful I don't take you at your word one night," said the German without conviction. I felt him jumping down from the truck.

"Shall we take a look at the goods?"

Somebody started rattling the metal object I had heard before. The truck shook as if something heavy had been chucked out. Then there was a long silence only broken by a regular wet thud on metal. I could picture the scene: three or four Germans in green uniforms devoutly bending over a fish crate, the contents of which were being transferred to a large German bucket. Suddenly I had a severe shock.

"Got room for another fish?" I heard Evald ask. Had he lost his mind? He was flouting the password of that morning right under the noses of the Germans.

But of course they wouldn't know. A moment later the

empty fish crate was thrown back into the compartment, the metal door clanged shut and the bolts rattled home. I straightened from my crouching position with considerable effort and stretched my frozen limbs. Then I remembered something. I bent down again and picked something off the floor. The strange, indefinite object that had clung to my feet was my faithful brown felt hat.

I slapped it on the crown as if it were an old friend with whom I wanted to share my relief. I was filled with a wonderful elation, as if I had just been acquitted of something or other, or successfully passed an exam. I even allowed myself a wide grin at Evald's last remark, now that it lay harmless in the past.

I heard the bolts on the trailer being drawn and shut again. Then there was another loud conversation up at the cab. The radio in the barracks started shouting out news: depressing reports from the front, which were immediately stifled. To the crackling and howling protest from the ether, somebody searched all over the dial for some more music. The Germans in front of the truck gave another roar of laughter. An automobile horn gave a long-drawn piercing blare. Slowly we started moving. The speed increased into the night.

# chapter two

Fifteen minutes later the rattling of the truck told me we were running on a surface of cobblestones. I realized that we were in Flensburg, but I wondered why we drove round the streets for so long. Eventually we pulled up, ran a bit forward, reversed carefully, moved forward again and finally stopped. Again I heard German voices. They sounded as if they came from a covered hall of some kind. They were low voices without any warmth of laughter. I braced myself for another long wait, when the bolts were suddenly drawn quietly aside, and the door was opened.

"Quick! Get out! Mingle with the others and don't ask too many questions!"

For the first time during the trip there was a note of impatience in Evald's voice.

Blinded even by the dim light that seeped through the open door, frozen stiff and greatly puzzled, I staggered down from the truck and came very close to flattening my nose against a charred black wall. Evald had backed right up beside it, so that I had to squeeze out sideways.

As far as I could see, we were in a large automobile repair shop. The place was illuminated by a couple of dim electric bulbs that threw a mercifully veiling light over mournful automobile wrecks, displaying their anatomical defects above yawning concrete trenches in the greasy floor. Five or six Germans in black leather jackets were gathered round Evald, who pointed at the driver's cab. The Germans followed his eyes, nodded and the group broke up. I made up my mind that this was none of my business, so I sauntered over and started scrutinizing an old passenger coach that had spent better and happier years peacefully linking village to village, but had now ended here as a derelict, disfigured by a coat of poisonous green and gray camouflage paint

From time to time I stole a glance at Evald's truck. Two of the leather-jacketed Germans were busy changing a front wheel tire. Evald came down from the cab with a cardboard box in his arms. The rest of the Germans drifted idly round the shop. Nobody approached me. It was as if they were afraid to see me.

By now it was past midnight. The scenery which at first had held a certain amount of morbid fascination was beginning to bore me. Since breakfast I had had neither food nor drink. I yawned abysmally with cold and weariness and wandered over to the truck. The Germans were still looking the other way as if on purpose. The back doors remained open. I climbed into the compartment and discovered two brand-new automobile tires occupying the space where I had been standing. I opened my case and transferred one of the hip flasks of cognac to my coat pocket. I could almost feel it warming my side through the pocket. When I ducked out of the darkness and returned to the door, I found myself looking straight down into Evald's beaming face.

"Feeling kind of homesick for the luxury suite?" he asked. I grabbed his hand. I wanted to say something really nice to

24

him. But I couldn't say it, as long as he stood there, laughing up into my face.

"You're off your head," I smiled at him. "Why did you have to make that crazy remark about room for one more fish?"

I think he understood what I was trying to say. He helped me down.

"I thought maybe you'd be bored stiff," he explained. "I just wanted to cheer you up a bit."

He banged the doors shut and fastened the bolts.

"Don't give the Jerries in here a thought. They are more scared of you than you need be of them. They only have one thought—to stay in business!"

His hand made a sweeping explanatory gesture from the new tires in the back of the truck to the cardboard box I had seen him bring out of the cab, and which was now being emptied by two of the Germans.

"Now let's get going. You can safely park down in your old seat beside the captain."

Once more we headed south. The big truck gripped the road steadily. Evald leaned comfortably back in the seat and lit a cigarette.

"No need to rush," he said. "It'll be soon enough if we hit Hamburg come six o'clock."

I pulled out the cognac flask and offered it to Evald. His face brightened as he took a long pull.

"Stuff certainly warms you," he sighed, wiping his lips.

I rolled the cognac slowly round on my tongue before I let it slip down my throat. It coursed through me like a stream of fire, and I felt the warmth slowly spreading out to all my limbs.

"You going on from Hamburg?" Evald finally asked. "Not that I'm nosy, but if you are going farther, I might give you a few tips."

"Yes, I'm going farther east," I said briefly, to discourage questioning.

Neither of us spoke for a while.

Naturally Evald was curious, and of course I couldn't tell him anything. But under different circumstances I might have given him a story that would have appealed to his taste for the dramatic.

It was warm in the cab and I was drowsy.

"Falling asleep?" he asked.

"I was dozing off," I replied.

"Sorry to wake you, but we're hitting Rendsburg in a minute. They might get nasty on the Kiel Canal bridge. How are you fixed with papers?"

I felt my inside pocket. "My passport should be all right. It's stamped for entry into Germany via Krusaa last night. I stamped it myself yesterday."

Evald grinned. "This is a dumb question, I guess, but why did you have to be smuggled across when you have good papers?"

There was nothing dumb about that question, but Evald could not be expected to know that traveling in my present capacity I had to avoid border posts at all costs. In wartime hardly any travelers cross the border officially, and the few who do are carefully checked and rechecked. Even the finest forgeries may be detected by the quick and comprehensive communication facilities found on every border post.

Evald was looking at me questioningly, and I hastened to give him an answer. "Because my friends found it safer this way. You've no idea how hysterical the Jerries are with papers. I dare say you can always get a truck across, but give them a passport and see how busy they can get."

"Don't get the idea that those Jerries at the border were the usual kind," said Evald with a hint of apology in his voice, as if deploring the fact that he hadn't provided me with sufficient excitement. "They were reserves, old men who are half dead on their feet and don't give a darn anyway. But they get tougher as you go further south—or east," he added encouragingly.

The Germans had closed the road at Rendsburg by means of a heavy barrier which they had placed just in front of the automobile and pedestrian bridge across the Kiel Canal. It was a strategic point of no little importance. The Kiel Canal is Germany's interior connecting route for war vessels between the North Sea and the Baltic. Another huge bridge construction leads the railroad from a considerable height down into the town.

We pulled up politely in front of the barrier which was dimly lighted by two lamps. Behind them I could just make out the first section of the bridge superstructure.

A sentry in green uniform rushed out of the darkness pointing his machine gun at the truck. He ordered us out of the cab and over to a long, low building of red brick, standing on the left side of the road.

The guard room was hot as a furnace inside. When Evald and I entered, we saw a fat German with his tunic unbuttoned, seated behind a table. He was bending over a book bound in black linen.

This time I decided to take the lead.

"Filthy weather tonight," I said rubbing my hands together. "Feels good to get indoors in the heat."

But the German did not seem to be the type who would contribute voluntarily towards making people feel at ease. Without saying a word he reached for Evald's passport, the papers of the truck, my passport and my traveling permit.

The guard commander, or whatever he was, flipped through the pages of Evald's passport and gave it a few stamps here and there. Then he settled himself comfortably in the chair, grabbed my passport, held it up in front of him and started scrutinizing it page by page. I knew that all forged entry and exit stamps from the German border were minute copies of the stamps currently in use. The stamps I carried on me were little technical wonders. The fellows in London had every right to be proud of them, but who could tell?—maybe someone had made a tiny error!

The German went on turning the pages. Now and then he referred to the book with the black linen cover, apparently to verify some information contained in the passport. The room got hotter and hotter. I felt my collar tighten uncomfortably round my neck. At last the guard commander put the passport down and started subjecting my traveling permit to the same thorough investigation. When at last he seemed to be through, he casually asked without raising his eyes from the permit, "Now let me see, you were in Germany in—1942? What month would that be?"

Oh, no you don't, my fine friend, I thought, changing my facial expression to one of strained reflection. I had studied those stamps and their dates until I knew them backwards in my sleep. After a suitable pause I answered,

"You must be mistaken, Herr Commander. I did not visit Germany in 1942. But I came here on business to Frankfurt in 1943, both in April and August."

The commander flipped through the pages once more for the sake of appearances. "In order!" he growled and stamped the passport.

The next moment the door flew open, and Willy came stumbling into the guard room, followed by the sentry. I underwent a sudden and startling change from complete confidence to panicky indecision. This could only mean that my suitcase had been discovered and the game was up, almost before it had started.

But to my intense relief it was not the fiber case the sentry placed on the table, but a cardboard box filled with little rectangular packages wrapped in tissue paper.

"Contraband butter!" reported the sentry dutifully and withdrew with a smart salute.

The guard commander's face turned deep purple. Here at last he had a chance of releasing all the spleen and irritation he had saved up, sitting night after night in a dump like Rendsburg.

He thumped his meaty fist on the table and rose to his full height which was far from being impressive.

"You're nothing but a mob of smugglers, you fish-truck drivers!" he roared. "This goes on time after time! You're laughing right up in our faces. But you've tried it once too often! This time I will make an example of you. I'll get you, get you." In his violent rage he searched around for the most terrible, the most inhuman and complicated means of execution, and it was something of an anti-climax when he finally exploded.

"—get you shot, Schweinehund!"

Evald stood with averted eyes, a touching picture of the repentant sinner. He answered in a low voice, speaking his impossible German:

"*Ja, das war nicht so gut, Herr Oberwachmeister*. Then we had better share it."

"Share?" screamed the commander, who had lost all interest in the nature of the crime and was instead concentrating on the goods involved. Not on your life! The butter is confiscated! It will remain here! You just be thankful if I let you off this time."

Evald looked helplessly around. For once his resources seemed to be exhausted. The threat of a firing squad had left him quite calm, but the prospect of losing his butter seemed to have made him desolate.

I decided that now was the time to call in the last reserves. "Pardon me, Herr Commander," I said and drew a long envelope out of my pocket. "I forgot to show you this."

The commander looked suspiciously at me, snatched the envelope and was just about to tear it open, when he caught sight of the eagle with a swastika in its claws, which graced the upper right corner of the envelope. He sat down at the table, unfolded the letter reverently and started reading.

It was a letter of recommendation from the German High Commissioner in Denmark, Dr. Werner Best, who called upon any German authority in question to assist the Danish businessman, Aage Schmidt, in every way possible. Herr Aage Schmidt had been of valuable service to the German occupation authorities in Denmark, and had thus qualified for the highest privileged treatment during his business trip to Berlin.

The commander folded up the letter, placed it in the envelope and handed it to me without a word. His expression indicated unconditional surrender. I received the compliment on behalf of my distant, unknown friends in London.

"Herr Evald Hansen has saved me a lot of trouble on this journey," I told the commander. "I suggest we settle this little matter by giving you the top layer of butter packages in the box—as a kind of reward for your watchfulness. The rest is a present for my—business connections."

I threw a significant look at the letter of recommendation. Its meaning was not lost on the commander.

When we were once more on our way, and the yellow lights on the barrier were flashing us a last injured look, Evald slapped me on the back and exclaimed with a laugh,

"That was great going! They'll never dare try anything on me again. I guess that letter must have been from Hitler himself?"

He retained the smile on his face, but his voice took on an earnest ring, as if he were very anxious that I should understand him.

"You must have caught on in Flensburg that I have a couple of little side lines. You can call it black market, smuggling, or anything you like. You have to be on your toes these days to keep going. All the same I'm glad you had that bit of paper. Otherwise I'm not sure I'd have made it back home. This truck doesn't run on beer, and especially not on that thin stuff they push at you in Germany today. A little butter is the only thing I have to trade for oil and petrol."

The darkness changed character. It was no longer the

dense velvety black, but had assumed a shiny, metallic hue as if it was being thinned out with more and more gray.

Around dawn—a miserable low-ceilinged February morning—the roads began to come to life. I wondered why the first people we saw coming out of the darkness were heading out of town. They plodded along at the side of the road, bending under the weight of bundles and trunks. In between we saw something that looked like a whole family, adults and children, pooling their strength to push a wagon or a cart filled with household goods.

"First refugees from East Prussia. Won't be long before they pay us a visit up north," said Evald, making a wry face.

Hamburg rose out of the receding darkness like a wild, shattered rock profile. We drove gingerly along a narrow road that had been cleared between mountains of stone and rubble made by the crumbling ruins. In the center of the road were trolley tracks, but they looked more like the tip-cart rails of a gigantic gravel pit.

Gray people were making their way into town along the narrow paths higher up the sides of the rubble heaps. Cold, hungry and exhausted. Without a word and with eyes staring rigidly ahead. A great city was waking to a new, pointless gray day. A giant torso with amputated limbs.

In the large, rectangular building of the fish-export market in Hamburg there were no apparent signs of activity. We backed our wagon-train through one of the main hall entrances. I jumped down and stretched myself with a loud creaking in all my limbs. Now if only I had a good warm cup of coffee! Evald fetched my suitcase from the truck and placed it in the cab, as if it were the most natural thing in the world. I looked around me. The workmen strolled about in the spacious hall, doing nothing useful. High up under the ceiling along the four inner walls of the building, there was a long gallery, a strange construction of trellis-work and bars. It looked alarmingly like a prison. I stole a glance at my suitcase. Oh, well, surely a traveling salesman was allowed to take some luggage.

"It'll take some time before they get her unloaded," Evald said and pointed to the trailer, which was now detached from the cab. He continued:

"So I suggest you come with me to see one of my business connections. He lives in a spot where I feel more at home. It isn't out of your way. In fact you'll be on the right road, and maybe I can fix you up with something from there. Unless you've had enough of rattling around in a truck? If you'd rather go by rail, I can drop you at the station."

This was a problem which I had given careful consideration. My traveling permit was in perfect order, but I still preferred to avoid a decisive test made by competent, experienced officials. At any control post of a railway station, or on a train going full speed, I would be caught in a very tight corner. At the highway barriers there were better chances of talking your way out of an unpleasant situation. I decided to accept Evald's offer.

We rattled past the main station, now looking like some huge burnt-out hangar with only the charred ribs still standing. From then on my sense of direction deserted me. I had thought I knew Hamburg in and out, but in a few moments I was completely lost. We were no longer driving through a city, but through a landscape of rocks. But Evald seemed to know the way perfectly.

"How the hell do you do it?" I asked him, peering desperately in all directions to find some familiar feature.

"Easy," he said. "It isn't me driving us. It's the truck. She's just smelling her way ahead."

"Smelling what?" I asked, puzzled.

"Diesel oil!" grinned Evald.

We ran past a section of ruins that beat everything I had seen to date. The finely ground rubble stretched as far as the eye could see, without a single upright feature to obstruct the view.

32

Judging by the time it took to drive past it, this continuous area of ruins must have covered most of a square mile. Every trace of streets, squares and roads was completely wiped out. The area was staked out in the craziest geometrical pattern. It looked like the gigantic, massive foundations of some mad venture.

I was filled with the awesome admiration people strangely enough always seem to feel when confronted with perfection— be it reason or madness.

For once even Evald had no comment to make.

Eventually the center of Hamburg lay behind us. From a low hill I looked back and saw the great city through a gray mist, mercifully veiling its shattered contours.

That stone quarry will never make a town again, I thought, taking a last look over my shoulder. The mist had obscured practically everything. There were only a few tall factory chimneys looming out of the swirling, gray sea. It was a strange paradox that the last thing I should see was the black smoke columns from the chimneys—like a last desperate bellow of smoke from a giant liner, disappearing into the sea.

We soon reached the vicinity of Bergedorf, one of the southeasterly suburbs of Hamburg and the main junction of all road traffic going east. We drove through an almost undamaged district. Dignified white houses lay well back from the road behind gardens that were now growing wild, but had no doubt boasted flourishing green lawns and bright flower beds before the war.

Evald slowed up in front of a magnificent iron gate.

"Is this where your business connections hang out?" I asked, much impressed.

Evald reached into the glove compartment, pulled out a packet of cigarettes and pushed it in his pocket.

"You're crazy," he said. "I don't move in these class circles. But we'll be there in a moment."

We stopped at a filling station on the highway to Berlin. There were two men in a little concrete hut behind the pump.

As we entered, a youngster looked up quickly from some accounts. When he saw who it was, his expression showed considerable relief.

"Take it easy, it's only me," said Evald. "Maybe you'd been expecting better company?" He flashed the men a knowing mischievous smile.

The other man greeted us by raising two fingers to the peak of his cap.

"Who's he?" asked the attendant and looked searchingly at me.

It struck me that he was the same type as Evald, with the same sharp features and the same quick eyes.

"A friend of mine," said Evald and offered him a cigarette.

The attendant wiped his fingers on a piece of cotton waste and lit the cigarette. "Business?" he asked.

"No, you can't sell him anything. He wants to go on east, if there's a chance. Got any suggestions?"

The man shook his head. "Not right off."

Evald's direct question told me that he trusted these people. I relaxed a bit. The German at the other side of the table was reading a newspaper. He was a bent-up old man with hands that shook slightly. I doubted if he caught on to any of what he was reading.

"I expect she's thirsty," said the young man nodding at the truck outside. "I'll go get the cans."

We followed him out the door. The old man in the chair didn't take the slightest interest. Evald drew me aside.

"They're okay," he whispered. "The son gets me diesel oil. He managed to get himself failed by the draft medical board—rheumatic fever I think—he lives from day to day scared stiff of being drafted, now they've come to the end of the reserves. The old man is his father. Former trade-union man. He's been in a concentration camp—to be brought up right and get a few misunderstandings ironed out. How old do you think he is?"

"Somewhere round seventy," I answered.

34

"Just on fifty. Go and talk to him, while I fix up this deal. But don't ask him any questions. He can't take it."

It was difficult starting a conversation with the old man. He parried all my efforts with words of one syllable. But from time to time he raised his eyes and looked at me searchingly. I discovered that his expression was not empty or dead, but merely distant, as if he saw everything from a completely different plane. I felt increasingly ill at ease under these appraising looks. Our conversation foundered, and I didn't like to talk about the weather. I had a feeling that this man had long been beyond such trivialities.

Then suddenly holding my gaze, he said,

"I expect Evald has told you I've been in a concentration camp. I was fit and healthy when the gates closed behind me. What you see now is all that managed to drag itself out."

There was a pause during which I felt strangely superfluous.

He leaned forward across the table and clenched his impotent, yellowish hand.

"Those bloody swine!" he whispered hoarsely, speaking more as a conclusion to his own thoughts than directly to me.

His gaze returned from a dark and faraway world and met mine. "I may be wrong, but I haven't got much more to risk. I don't believe you are any ordinary traveling salesman. But no matter what firm you represent, I'd like to help you."

For the first time there was the shadow of a smile on his face. A smile of resignation.

"Maybe I can't do much, but what little help I can give you, I offer you with pleasure. I was in the concentration camp for three years. If I'm going back there, it won't be for nothing. Remember, I've given them three years in advance!"

His eyes were no longer vacant. There was no doubt that he meant what he said.

"If it should happen during the next few months that you and your son are visited by business people who can give you

35

the license number of Evald's truck, would you try to help them on their way?"

He nodded. Then he bent over the newspaper again. The fire in his eyes slowly died out. In his world there was nothing more to discuss.

A moment later Evald, returning with the son, placed the box of butter packages on the table. I looked at it. Together with the guard commander at Rendsburg it had already become a faded, distant memory. Had all this really happened last night?

We all sat down at the table. Evald teetered like a daring tightrope walker over the pitfalls of the German language. Now and then he had to get busy with the balancing pole, using a whole sentence of unadulterated Danish, but he succeeded in painting a colorful and fairly clear picture of the nocturnal battle of the butter at Rendsburg.

The son brought out some bread and sausages. I fetched another flask of cognac from the suitcase and passed it round. Evald warmed up and started talking of other skirmishes he had taken part in at night. The cosy atmosphere made me quite drowsy.

We were just approaching the inevitable and dramatic climax of one of Evald's romantic escapades, when a motor horn honked impatiently outside. The son got up and went out. A moment later he returned and beckoned to Evald, who also disappeared.

After a time Evald opened the door and waved me outside.

"I think we have a solution," he said and pointed to a small car parked in front of the pump.

At first I thought it was some tradesman's van, then I caught sight of the Red Cross on the sides and the Danish national emblem on the bonnet, and realized that it was an ambulance.

"Now here's a chap who has been sent out all alone in the wide and wicked world," sighed Evald without any hint of sarcasm. "He's going to Torgau near Dresden to have a little look at a concentration camp. It's his first trip and he's a bit nervous. I can't say I blame him. He doesn't know the road, and he doesn't know the ropes. If you're going that way, I guess you ought to help him out a bit. You'll be doing him a favor."

I considered the possibilities. My papers were in order. There was nothing in my suitcase which a businessman shouldn't have, or at least nothing that would compromise the Red Cross. As it happened it was part of my job to get information about the distribution and reshuffling of prisoners of war and other internees in Germany. I found it quite justifiable to interpret these orders as a kind of parallel to the Red Cross man's job. Above all this was a fantastic, unexpected opportunity which would never come again.

The Red Cross driver, dressed in a baggy blue uniform of some thick material, was talking to the young German.

"What a bit of luck that you're going the same way!" he said when I walked over to him. "It all seems a bit—a bit overwhelming at first," he added apologetically.

He was at the same time a picture of determined courage and touching helplessness. A fellow alone with his ambulance. A lone fireman with his little waterbucket right in the middle of the biggest blaze in history. And he was going first to Berlin.

Evald put my suitcase in the ambulance and drew me aside for a moment.

"Look here," he said—and for the first time he seemed to be searching for words—"I think we had a great time together. You're a good guy and I'd like to stick around an' see the end of this game. But you know how it is"—he gestured vaguely towards the north—"somebody waiting for me up there, and they don't sleep well, till I get back. But what I said yesterday about the five hundred—just pretend you haven't heard it. Not that it isn't good sense, because it is, but I'd like this to be a favor from me to you."

I grabbed his hand. "I'm glad to hear you say that, Evald."

"Good luck," he said and gave me a friendly pat on the back. "By the way, I was talking through the top of my head. Thank God I'm not in your shoes!" he added with his mischievous smile.

The ambulance had already started moving when I suddenly remembered something.

"Hey, Evald!" I shouted.

He came running up and stuck his head through the window.

"What kind of devilry was it you let loose in the truck last night at the border? All those little creepy-crawly things. They gave me a terrific scare."

For a while he looked at me without understanding. Then his lips parted in an enormous grin, the widest I had seen on the whole trip. "Lobsters, you dope! You were standing right up against a crate of live lobsters!"

# chapter three

The steel helmet squeezed my head uncomfortably as if I had put on some other man's hat by mistake. Apart from that I found it rather ridiculous here on Kurfurstendamm, the main street in western Berlin, which, judging by the beams of light along the sidewalk and the sparks from the trolley wires overhead, was still a street with shops and public transport facilities rather than a sector of the front.

"I guess I can take this off now," I told the Danish Red Cross man whose name was Kristian. I removed the steel saucepan and had the pleasant feeling that my brain returned to its normal size. Maybe that was why it hadn't been functioning too brightly since we left Hamburg.

"But don't think I haven't been mighty glad you brought a spare one along," I went on in a conversational effort to make up for my silence all afternoon. "You never know what can happen on a road journey these days."

"I think it went unbelievably smoothly," said Kristian. "I'll never forget the way those green soldiers jumped for us at the road barriers by Ludwigslust and Perleberg. They were bowing and scraping as if we had been diplomats."

His slightly overconfident tone revealed the first-day tourist, who already knows the whole world.

"Well, you represent the only diplomatic corps they still have a grain of respect for," I said, glancing at the Red Cross band on his arm. "And who knows how long that will last? No, I guess you'd better keep the battle bowler well down around your ears on your trip south. . . . By the way, are you spending the night in Berlin?"

Kristian spotted a heap of rubble just in time to pull around it.

"No, I've decided to do the trip in one stretch. The people expecting me have already been waiting for two or three years. I guess I can afford to give up a night's rest for them," he added somewhat embarrassed.

I pressed his arm gently and bent down to open my suitcase.

"Here you are," I said, handing him a carton of American cigarettes. I had wanted to offer him some before, but I hadn't wanted to invite too many questions.

"There's no need to pay me for the trip," he said hesitatingly.

"You take them. They're just as good as ready cash—even better." I put the carton on the seat beside him. Then I closed the suitcase again but kept hold of the handle.

"We've just about reached the spot where I get off," I said, searching for the trail of light in the darkness.

"Good luck!" Kristian shouted, when I stood on the sidewalk with the suitcase in my hand. Involuntarily I looked around me and then put two fingers to my hat. A moment later the little ambulance had been swallowed up by the darkness.

I crossed the road and continued down Kurfurstendamm,

carefully keeping count of the streets after Brandenburgische Strasse.

When I had walked for five minutes, I turned left down a side street where I kept equally careful count of the house numbers on the right-hand side. I stopped at number eleven, opened the heavy, wide entrance door and stepped into a stately hall, flanked by two massive black marble slabs that made me think of princely burials of the past. Slender, almost frivolous little vases softened the somber lines of the marble sarcophaguses, and above them were huge mirrors, fashioned for a now extinct race of Germanic giants.

On the fourth floor I fumbled for the doorbell—the snout of an impressive gilded lion's head, placed at the right of the door. I pushed in the lion's snout and waited anxiously. After a while I heard the sound of a door being opened inside the apartment and voices reached my ears.

Then the door opened and a face came gradually into sight. First a slightly ruffled, ash-blond lock of hair, then a nose, which for no apparent reason widened towards the extremity as if an extra lump had been hurriedly slapped onto it at the last moment, and finally a long chin.

I held my hand out with a smile.

"I have company," he whispered. "I'll try to get rid of them. Come back in an hour's time."

I pointed to the suitcase.

He took it and placed it inside the hall, winked at me and closed the door.

Once more I strolled down Kurfurstendamm, wondering how I should pass the time. Here and there I could see faint beams of light, like peepholes into mourning chapels dimly lit by wax candles. I chose one of them, which turned out to be the Ufa Palatz movie house on Kurfurstendamm. The extra had just started as I slid into a seat in one of the back rows. It was a newsreel showing a crashed Flying Fortress, photographed from every conceivable angle. The film had been cut up and pasted together again to make it seem that they brought down a whole squadron.

"We have changed the Flying Fortresses into Flying Coffins," said the commentator triumphantly, but apparently without the least response from the audience, who for the most part were sitting here because the commentator's Flying Coffins had made a mess of the places where they would otherwise have spent their evening.

The main feature was a stupid farce, starring Theo Lingen and Hans Moser. They did their best but the audience received their anachronistic slapstick in stony silence. I felt the cold spreading out both physically and mentally.

I sat watching the gray shadows of Messrs. Lingen and Moser, without really seeing them. Instead I thought of Carl with whom I had just left my suitcase.

The first time I had heard of him was half a year ago back in Stockholm at a small, select party, where somebody had told the story of a Swedish businessman in Berlin who hated the Nazis. He gathered together a small circle of people—both Germans and Swedes—who shared his opinions. They met once a week in his apartment for the purpose of sharing their hatred, and the object on which they poured their mutual disdain was, according to our informant, a large lithograph of a snow-white stallion carrying an armor-clad knight with a waving banner in one hand. Through the half-open visor of the helmet you could see a small mustache and a pair of piercing, suspicious eyes. This Hitler lithograph bore the legend *Der Bannertrager* (The Standard Bearer). It was in bad taste and very rare because it was banned throughout Germany. Even the Nazi party got sore eyes looking at it.

I didn't think more about the story until some time later, when I had finished my training and was trying to find a foolproof cover address in Berlin. It seemed to be hopeless. Even our most indirect feelers were turned down with all signs of terror. The conception of a resistance movement seemed to be completely unknown in Berlin. I racked my brain, but the only thing I could get out of it, time and time again, was the story of the Swede with *Der Bannertrager*. It kept turning up, no matter how hard I tried to get rid of it, and finally in desperation I got the O.S.S. to investigate the man's connections.

The result was, mildly speaking, a surprise. We arranged that the Swedish businessman should come to Stockholm, where I spent three days with him from morning till night. I talked to him, watching his reactions and putting him to certain tests. All came to the same conclusion: He was a man endowed with common sense and imagination, well-informed and with a revulsion against Nazidom based on something fundamental in his character, something almost religious—honest goodness and respect for his fellow men. On the third day I initiated him into my plans and suggested that he should become my assistant in Berlin.

I had expected a long silence full of ponderous reflection, but Carl had waved his hand impatiently.

"Yes, yes, of course! Consider that settled. Why else would I have come up here?"

Carl returned to Berlin and for security reasons we had not been in touch personally with each other since then. I could only hope that he hadn't changed since that night in Stockholm. It was a gamble like everything else in my line. You plan as carefully as you like beforehand, but in the end the outcome is always a matter of chance. You pick a number, and you just have to hope it's going to pay off. . . .

My attention returned to the film, which had reached the stupid climax of all such films, where one person, dressed as another, unexpectedly meets a third in the bed of a fourth. There was a sudden commotion at the rear of the theater. The lights went on and a voice from the loudspeaker requested everyone to remain quietly in their seats. I looked around me bewildered, until I saw the exit. The doors were blocked by a row of gray-green military police. Other gray-green uniforms were moving down the aisles. Heavy footbeats resounded hollowly in the theater.

Most of the audience took this with the same apathetic calm with which they had received the film. A few, I among them, started fumbling nervously in their pockets. A young man sitting in the same row as myself but a few seats nearer the aisle caught my attention when, with a slight nod, his head fell forward. Were the people of Berlin so used to police raids that they could fall asleep right in the middle of them?

The M.P.'s took up position in pairs at the end of each row and summoned people one by one. A curt command, a quick check-up of cards and papers, a brief nod and a German would be shuffling back to his seat. The raid moved methodically and almost silently up to my row without anything untoward happening. The Germans at the end of the row showed their papers and sat down again. The young man who was dressed in thin, worn dungarees and an old leather jacket was still fast asleep. I cleared my throat to make my voice ready to answer the inevitable questions cheerfully and preferably in a nonchalant tone. Another German returned to his seat and gave the young sleeper a gentle nudge. He rose with a start and stumbled over his neighbor's feet out towards the aisle. So that was the trouble! He was drunk. I completely forgot where I was and leaned expectantly back in my seat. The unpredictable collisions of drunks and police had always amused me far more than the craziest film comedy.

One of the M.P.'s, a tall dark man with eyes set so close together that they almost seemed like a single black slit under his bushy eyebrows, reached a hand towards the young fellow, who was shifting his weight unsteadily from one leg to the other, as if the center of gravity kept moving beneath him.

I heard him launch into a mumbling explanation, which the M.P. interrupted with an impatient gesture. Suddenly the young man recovered his balance and took off, tearing down the aisle like a wild bull with lowered head.

The M.P. hardly turned his head. "Deserter!" he shouted, and beckoned the next man in the row to step out.

The young German only got about ten yards down the aisle before other policemen were on him. He disappeared in a huddle of gray-green uniforms, and for a moment I could only see a flurry of arms methodically working up and down like flails. Then the group broke up. The young man was lying on the floor without moving, his head covered by his arms. Two policemen pulled him up by the shoulders and dragged him out of the theater.

The faces of most of the audience were completely closed up, devoid of any expression of feeling. Nobody turned around to watch the young man being taken off. Only the people sitting nearest followed, from the corners of their eyes, the unconscious youth being dragged between the two hefty M.P.'s.

"It's your turn. Are you asleep?" said the impatient voice of the M.P. and I was startled that he was speaking to me. I stumbled out of the row—just as agile as the young man, I cursed myself inwardly.

"Foreigner?" The German looked up from my passport. "What is the reason for your visit to Berlin?"

"Business! It's all down there in the visa."

"What kind of business?"

"Buying electrical articles," I said, repeating my cover story. If he wanted it, I could give him a specification of bulbs, fittings, switches and leads down to the last watt and the last screw.

The Nazi sent me a cold, suspicious glare through the slit under his eyebrows, as if he were facing a man who had just admitted his intention to rob him of his last electric light bulb. He bent over the passport again.

"You arrived in Berlin today? Where are you staying? Who are your business connections?"

45

His questions rained down on me—just the approach I had been warned against, and against which my cover story should act as an umbrella. But who would have thought I should land in the middle of a raid within one brief hour before I could be sure Carl's address was safe.

I straightened up with dignity and put a hand on the back of the seat.

"If you will kindly let me answer your questions in some kind of order . . ." I said in a slightly huffy tone. "First of all may I be permitted to express my surprise at the reception which a friend of Germany gets on the first day of his visit to Berlin. I had expected that down here you would also know how to discriminate between people. At least the German authorities in Denmark know that much. Why do you suppose they issued me that visa?"

I snatched the passport from his hand and whacked a finger down on the stamps. "Do you suppose they give that to everyone? Oh, no, that is a privileged mark of trust only granted to people who have proved their honest will to contribute towards the reconstruction of Europe. It will be a pleasure to answer your questions," I went on, raising my eyebrows and choosing one he wouldn't have asked anyway:

"My visit to Berlin is partly for business purposes, but also" —I waved a hand round the theater and pointed to the screen— "a recreation trip to get my nerves in order. My collaboration with Germany has cost me my entire business. It was sabotaged a month ago. Everything that I had built up during the past ten years. Gone! Blown up!"

I paused to let the explosion settle in his ears.

The Nazi looked longingly after his colleague who was already three rows further down.

"What are your connections here in Berlin?" he asked taking out his notebook.

"*Nordische Wirtschaftselle und Verbindungsstelle für Aus-*

*landshandel,*" I improvised without batting an eyelid. I had to run that risk. It would be equally great whether or not these impressive sounding departments of German state administration existed.

He scribbled down the names. "And what was your name?"

I handed him my passport with an overbearing patient smile. I got it back together with a contemptuous glare.

When I finally sat opposite Carl in one of the huge armchairs in his study, the warmth that had been lacking in the welcome of the German authorities was more than compensated for.

"I've been worried about you!" said Carl jumping up from his chair for the tenth time. "I've been expecting you for the past two months and oddly enough I mostly kept a lookout late in the evening. I used to slip around over by the little park across the street around eleven P.M. expecting to see you appear out of the bushes any moment, as we had planned in Stockholm. Every time the sirens went I thought it was in your honor!"

He grinned, stroking one stubborn lock of hair away from his forehead. He might be thirty years old and he might be forty. His smooth face, supple as a sculptor's clay under his constantly changing expressions did not reveal his age.

"And now you turn up in a quiet, civilized way with your suitcase, ringing the doorbell like any other traveler who has just come up on the train! Then you disappear again and run smack into a police raid, something I've never been lucky enough to experience! No, as I have said to myself ever since I met you in Stockholm, that fellow——"

He mentioned my real name.

I put my hand in the air like a traffic cop. "Hold it. That man does not exist here. He doesn't exist at all any more. You are now facing your old pre-war business acquaintance, Aage

47

Schmidt, a gentleman who has developed along rather unfortunate lines. A collaborator who got cold feet in his own country and has now come here for a rest.

"Yes, sir! Aage Schmidt, black market tycoon, with an insatiable lust for life before everything goes to pieces! Devil-may-care, because he knows he will always come to the surface like a piece of cork. A typical salesman, not representing the noble and discreet old firm you think, but working for Nazi-Europe Ltd., on the verge of bankruptcy. A dangerous gent to trifle with—unscrupulous—especially for a weak soul like yourself, who will keep seeing him, because he has infected you. You will take on his tone, copy his slang. You will become a pain in the neck to your former acquaintances, because you will get an increasing taste for Aage Schmidt's vicious circle. You have already come a long way down in the course of this evening."

Carl pinched his nose, the way he always did when he was thoughtful. "Yes, this role sounds fine, especially when we start——"

I got up quickly. "We'll get to that later," I said. "First of all the most important thing: Has the courier service been working as planned? Have the shipments got through?"

Carl gave me a crafty smile, walked over to the outer wall of the room, fingered the wallpaper until a section came open, disclosing a large rectangular space. He pointed into the yawning dark hole, enjoying my amazement.

"Tricky, isn't it?" he asked. "It has cost me many hours of work. But it was worth it."

I looked into the hole and could make out packages and cardboard boxes piled in long rows.

"There is as much in the other room and some in the kitchen. The transmitters have their own little broadcasting station which I have built down in the cellar and covered up with a pile of cinders." He waved his hand like a host proudly showing a guest round the house. "I don't think a single shipment has gone astray," he went on. "Everything has gone like clockwork.

The couriers have turned up punctually at the places you told me. We exchanged passwords and they handed me their packages, then set a date for the next meeting. I just don't understand how you made it all work so smoothly."

I patted him on the shoulder. "Even the best of friends can keep a few secrets to themselves, you know. For the time being at least," I hastily added when I saw the look of disappointment on his face.

I looked appraisingly round the room.

"We've got weapons, we've got medical supplies, we've got black market goods, radio transmitters, German and foreign currency, false stamps and, last but not least, we have a good chain of couriers working."

"Well, what are we waiting for?" said Carl, fixing up the wallpaper again.

I led him over to the armchair, where I poured drinks for both of us.

"It won't be all on our own, Carl," I said. "A lot of things have happened since we last met. The project is bigger than ever. It's no longer a matter of individuals but of a combined operation. We have a score of men of various nationalities training in London. They'll be schooled as saboteurs and later they'll mingle with the foreign workers here in Berlin. It is my job to pave the road for them, make contacts.

"This is one part of our mission," I continued. "The other is to act as the secret listening apparatus of O.S.S. in Berlin. We are the only ones here for the time being. We've got to be on the spot when something really important happens, inquisitive, but without showing it. We have to keep an eye on the effects of air raids on the factories and traffic in the city, on the subway, 'S-bahn' and the trolley system. We have got to gauge the spirit of the people and watch for any changes in morale. We must listen to scraps of street conversation and jokes—if there are still any—keep up to date with changes in the daily life, rationing cards, supplies, the shortages of certain commodities and

49

maybe a sudden surplus of others, outdoor life, posters, amusements, restaurants——"

"How the hell do we get the time for all that?" Carl said dubiously. "Do you realize that there are four million people in Berlin?"

"Sure, I know that," I said. "But there's the black market, Carl! Have you ever thought what a hotbed of news and gossip that is? I'm a bad guesser if it proves much different here than in the occupied countries, where it has all the news long before anyone else. I've thought the whole thing out carefully. It may be unorthodox, but it is the most direct line. We'll compare everything we hear with what we see ourselves or find out from reliable sources. And when we've checked everything to the best of our ability, we'll make out a report and send it off to London."

"On the transmitter?" Carl asked wistfully.

"No, we'll use the couriers while they're still working. In that way we can make our reports longer and more comprehensive."

"You're quite right," he said, "in assuming that the black market is running Berlin right now. Everybody's in it, the army, the party——"

"That's just it," I interrupted. "Those are the people we want to get at. We're going to work our way right into where the big shots are sitting. What they daren't tell each other, they may tell their black-market suppliers. And what they would rather die than think in a sober state, they may well blurt out when they have had one too many."

"Well, how do we start our black market career?"

"From the bottom, how else?" I said.

He shot out of his chair, rushed over to me and shook me by the lapels. "You've become so damned secretive since I last saw you—Mr. Schmidt. What part have you thought up for me? Private chauffeur for the black market tycoon?"

I freed myself, smiling. "In this job there are advantages when the right hand doesn't know everything the left is doing.

When I don't tell you about the courier service right away, it's not my doing. It's only to safeguard the organization—and you—if anything should happen." I pressed his arm gently. "As for the job of private chauffeur, it's yours, but not in the car you're driving now—if it answers to your description. I intend to ride in style. Incidentally that's where we start in on the black market."

Carl looked at me in horror.

"The Smoke Screen? You're not asking me to turn her in? If I've told you anything unfavorable about that excellent vehicle, it's only been in fun. That's a hell of a memory you've got!"

"Dream about it tonight," I said, stifling a yawn. After all, I hadn't slept for more than forty-eight hours. "You can keep the Smoke Screen a while, but we'll soon need something better."

# chapter four

"What in heaven's name is this?" I called to Carl the next morning, as I stared wide-eyed at a strange procession plodding down the corridor. Two fat sausages came waddling along on tiny, skinny legs, one stuck right on the tail of the other as if they were joined by an invisible string.

"What do you mean?" Carl shouted from the bathroom, where he was shaving.

"The pantry's come alive," I said hastily stepping aside to make way for two dogs headed with great determination, straight for the bathroom door, which was suddenly opened. They made small piping noises and breathlessly tried to raise their bellies from the floor, without success.

"Pantry?" Carl said indignantly. "What are you talking about? Those are my two grand little dachshunds." He bent down so that a few blobs of soap from his foaming face landed on the back of one. This unexpected burden made it collapse flat against the floor.

53

"Love me, love my dogs," Carl went on firmly, and tenderly wiped the soap from the dog's fur. "They're the best dogs in the world."

"And the oldest," I said. "Are they intended for the marble mausoleum downstairs?"

Carl ignored my remark. "This is Uncle Otto." He pointed at the first sausage. "And the girl there is Aunt Elfie. . . . Say howdedo to the nice gentleman," he coaxed.

A quiver ran through the bodies of the two dogs.

"There! That's killed them!" I exclaimed frightened.

"Nonsense!" Carl answered impatiently. "They're just not used to getting up this early. They think it's still night. But they're good watchdogs. You can see for yourself that they've got the scent of someone new in the house."

Slowly Uncle Otto turned a gray, furrowed head towards me and sent me a fleeting, indifferent look that told me its owner had long since lost interest in the petty trifles of this world. Then with a terrific effort he turned his tail to me. Fascinated, I noticed that Uncle Otto did not walk on his paws but sank right down on the elbows with his paws flapping in front like small, absurd flippers.

"Uncle Otto has been looking forward to your visit," Carl declared proudly. "And Aunt Elfie too!"

Aunt Elfie's blinking, blind eyes followed Uncle Otto's tail, describing its half circle. Her fur was worn away right down to the roots, like an old threadbare rug.

"Now there's just one missing," Carl said, "and then we'll all be here. But you won't see the person in question before tonight," he added with a secretive smile.

While we were having our morning coffee, the real stuff from the couriers' stores, the sirens started wailing. First a few in the neighborhood answered with the snarl of others farther away, until it seemed that all the sound waves of the great city were colliding above the rooftops with wild, ear-splitting disharmony.

54

"Here we go again," said Carl walking calmly before me into the corridor, where he picked up a small suitcase. "Incidentally, it's not a bad idea—getting the risk spread around a bit." He pointed to the hidden hole behind the wallpaper.

There were only a few people in the cellar—mainly women, in wicker chairs or old armchairs, sitting quietly with their hands in their laps. They were scattered around the large room as if everyone had her own particular place. By the side of each chair there was a small suitcase resembling Carl's.

Suddenly the strange, tense silence was broken by some violent thudding explosions. This was my first serious air raid, and I didn't like it. The crashes became more and more frequent and finally merged into a steady rumbling peal of thunder. I thought I could feel the walls of the cellar shaking and threw an anxious look at the pale, flickering electric lamps fixed in the beam supports. It was queer to have come on this bright morning directly from the breakfast coffee down to a cavern with eerie, ghostly lighting and to hear the elements going crazy over your head.

"It's only the ack-ack," said Carl, suddenly remembering that I was not acclimatized. "Much ado about nothing," he whispered encouragingly.

I received his information with a halfhearted smile.

The housewives sat apathetically in their chairs. The thunder rolled on with unceasing force. Carl shifted around as if he were bored. "Doesn't look as if they're heading our way today," he said finally and got up. "Let's get up to the apartment and see what's going on."

Quite a lot had been going on for the past twenty minutes, it appeared. A gigantic, thick, black column of smoke was rolling in across East Berlin and the government quarters, swallowing one street after another and wiping out the towers and spires as it soared upwards. At brief intervals there was a kind of shimmer at the bottom of the billowing cloud, illuminated as by a giant flash of lightning. I strained my ears to hear the crash of the bombs, but could only make out the roaring of the ack-ack guns and occasionally the clatter of shrapnel against the rooftops.

"Look! There they are!" cried Carl with awe in his voice, as he pointed at the sky.

I raised my head. The dome of the sky, curving over Berlin like an empty, shiny bowl when the sirens sounded, had now, as if with giant plows, been divided by long gray-white furrows that started as wedges, where the plowshare dug in, and stretched back as long, dead-straight lines. I strained my eyes to find the invisible plows and at last, way up in the pale blue sky, I caught sight of them, twinkling in the sunshine—tiny, little objects in V-formation hardly recognizable as aircraft but more like flashes of light in the sky.

With unshakable calm, drawing their airy tracks behind them, the planes disappeared behind the dirty wall of smoke covering East Berlin. Small dirty-brown tufts were detaching themselves from the smoke belt and dotting the sky around the celestial plow furrows. But the flak shells had little effect. I only saw two of the tiny silver-gray machines circle downwards in long, smoking spirals. As the stricken aircraft grew larger, I could see small dots breaking away from them. Some of these dots continued their fluttering descent towards the earth, faster than the machine; others stopped and in an instant changed to white, billowing parachutes, celestial flowers suddenly blooming from the tiny, black seeds deep in the sky.

It all seemed like a lofty, cool and impersonal demonstration on the vast blackboard of the sky, showing the strategy of the air raid, the results of which were still hidden under the smoke wall, swelling to still greater dimensions with taut, red veins inflamed and about to burst open.

That afternoon we drove in Carl's automobile as far into the stricken area as barriers would allow. It was like driving on the edge of a world about to crumble. The corner houses were standing like the flaming portals of avenues of fire. Even the pavement was burning in places, where the gas pipes had burst. Elsewhere the water mains had broken and flooded the streets that lay like dirty, bubbling lakes with the flickering glow from the burning buildings reflected in the ripples. We drove in a weird, reddish gloom, and all around us there was an uncanny quiet. We could only hear the crackling of the flames, interrupted now and then by the muffled explosion of a time-bomb near by, or the rumbling thunder of a wall crashing down to earth.

We came past the huge slaughter-houses with row after row of charred beasts behind the collapsed walls, and we looked down streets where there were more charred animals, shackled to their still burning vehicles.

People were straying about like bewildered extras, who have suddenly become superfluous but still hang around on the set. Most of them carried some object that appeared pathetically stupid in these surroundings—a bucket, a small bundle, some household goods, a pair of boots—things they had happened to grab in their panic, when the stage suddenly collapsed.

Their faces were like those of sleepwalkers, lifeless and empty with shock. Some, in silent groups, stared with swollen red-rimmed eyes at their houses burning down, as if they were watching the inevitable effect of some law of nature. Others had protected their eyes with flying helmets, goggles or gas masks against the stinging, bitter smoke, and had desperately started shoveling half a collapsed apartment house away from the cellar entrance. The glow from the fires, mirrored in their goggle-glasses, had a macabre, almost supernatural effect. They looked like conquerors from a distant planet, their huge, bulbous eyes searching for treasure in the ruins they had brought about.

As we drove back, the giant bonfire was a bitter taste on my tongue and a stinging in my eyes, but otherwise the street scene was normal enough. Perhaps the trolleys were more crowded than usual and the stream of automobiles thicker on the two traffic lanes, but only a few pedestrians stopped to look towards the smoke wall in the east. A large poster stuck on the side of a ruined wall caught my eye. It was ragged and torn by wind and weather and the red color of the headline looked like dried blood against the naked bricks. I spelled my way through it: "THE STRONGER THE STORM—THE GREATER OUR RESISTANCE."

Carl followed my eyes. "It's a strange city," he said, shaking his head. "You can chop off one of its limbs, but the strength remains in its body, spreading out into the organs that are still functioning."

He pulled up hard at a pedestrian crossing. People walked across the street, housewives, old folk, some dressed in working clothes, some in uniforms, tired eyes, gray faces, each busy with his own thoughts with never a glance at the fellow beside him, busy but without undue haste, eager to get on but without signs of nervousness or panic.

"They're a tough race, the Berlin folk," Carl went on, while I watched them filing past. "Made of a special hard material, without much feeling for others, but then they don't expect others to feel anything for them either."


It was difficult to detach oneself at a moment's notice, to forget the crackling flames and the crumbled walls, the empty eyes and the pattern of tears on cheeks smeared with soot, dispassionately transcribing it all to a blueprint of what might presumably remain when the smoke wall had cleared. As yet I had no experience in construing shattered human destinies statistically, measuring the fear of death in square miles. For that reason it took me a long time to write out my first report.

When at last I completed it and straightened up from the paper, I could tell by the low hum of voices coming from the living room that Carl's little exclusive circle had already arrived. I fixed my tie, trying with a quick gesture to brush all the events of the afternoon away from my eyes, opened the door and stepped into the living room.

The first thing that caught my eye was *Der Bannertrager* standing on the polished mahogany table. He returned my look with an evil scowl through the half-open visor. I could not help feeling it was out of place. What I had found an amusing and daring joke six months ago in Stockholm, now seemed to me— here in Berlin after all I had seen that day—insignificant, stupid, flat and in very bad taste.

I turned my face away and noticed, farther back in the room, a tall, stooped man fixing me with a dark, inscrutable look. His black, gluey-looking hair that needed cutting fell down over his forehead like the eaves of a roof, accentuating the shadows of his haggard, bony face. Carl turned away from him and faced me.

"This is Mr. Schmidt, whom I have mentioned to most of those present," he said in general introduction. There was a slight pause in the conversation. Ill at ease I found myself the center of everyone's attention.

Smilingly Carl tried to set the ball rolling. "Mr. Schmidt is anxious to do his part in closing the visor completely on our friend there!" He pointed to the picture.

Without a word the tall, dark man came and shook my hand. He remained standing in the middle of the floor, and I could feel his searching eyes in my back as I turned to the next guest.

"You are a Swede, Mr. Schmidt?" a small, slightly dried-up woman asked, nimbly jumping up from her seat and holding my hand in an unexpectedly tight grip. Everything had been done as far as feminine skill was concerned to smooth out the wrinkles in her face. A gray-blonde lock of hair lay in a frivolous curl over her forehead.

"I adore and admire the Swedish nation," she continued eagerly without waiting for me to answer, her bright eyes smiling flirtatiously up at me.

I managed to express my regrets that I was not a Swede.

"Oh, but you are Scandinavian, aren't you? I am so looking forward to a talk with you. There is one of your countrymen standing over there, another Scandinavian."

I followed her eyes. By the window stood a thin, slightly built man smoking a cigarette. He was wearing a gray suit that appeared much too big for him, but there was something in his careless posture and the nonchalant way he held his cigarette that told me he knew it and didn't give a damn.

"He's the silent kind! You know, from the great, big, dark forests," the woman whispered feigning a shiver. "I do hope you are not like that."

The man by the window stubbed his cigarette out in the ashtray and lit another, glancing at the black-out curtain. I felt that here was at least one of the party whose thoughts were also circling round the smoke-wall in the east.

I looked despairingly around to find some way of escaping the talkative woman. A small, fat man with glasses, sitting right behind her and nursing his pipe in his hands, as if he were warming himself by it, caught on to my distress and leaned towards me waving the pipe.

"Before the war I used to visit Stockholm quite often," he said. "Tell me, Mr. Schmidt, are there still as many pretty girls at Skansen in the evenings. I remember——"

"Mr. Schmidt is not Swedish," the woman interrupted him sourly. She could feel me slipping through her fingers.

"Even so, Mr. Schmidt might know if there are still. . . ."

The woman and the little fat man continued their meaningless squabble about Mr. Schmidt, who hastened to remove himself out of their hearing.

I caught Carl's eye and shrugged my shoulders in a hopeless gesture. He looked at me without understanding.

Just then the doorbell rang. Carl grabbed *Der Bannertrager* and quickly threw it into a sideboard drawer. He went out to open the door. The lively woman cut herself short in the mid-

60

dle of an acid sentence, put her head on one side and said uncertainly to the fat man with the glasses, "I do hope it is
only. . . ."

It was. I smiled ironically. It was the very two types that
had been needed to complete the picture of a cosy get together
at the turn of the century. A skinny, large-boned man, wearing
a stiff, white collar and black coat, stepped into the room with
small polite bows. In his wake came a very young girl in a well-
cut suit that clung to her supple, softly rounded hips. Her eyes
wandered round the room, apparently looking for something,
and finally came to rest on me. She blushed, as if she had read
in my eyes admiration of her shapely figure, and took refuge
behind Carl.

Absent-mindedly I exchanged greetings with the clergy-
man. Carl squeezed the young girl's arm with the air of the
proud possessor and gave her something of the same tender look
he had used on Uncle Otto and Aunt Elfie that morning.

Now the family is gathered. Everyone's here, I thought
ironically. I paid my mark-note like all the rest and found an
armchair in a far corner of the room. What a group! It was a
terrible disappointment. These worthy and probably well-
meaning Germans meeting here in comfortable, safe surroundings, rolling down the black-out curtain to hide all the unpleas-
antness outside and soothing their conscience by sacrificing a
mark-note to some venture involving no risk for themselves.
Nice people, cultivated, well-mannered . . . oh, yes, all with
horribly nice manners! I looked around the assembly. A picture
of civic virtue and prudence. In these surroundings even Carl
looked more like a genial host in slippers than one of the Allies'
first secret contacts in Berlin.

I noticed that the thin man by the window occasionally
glanced over at me. He had a knowing, slightly ironical smile.
The remainder of the party seemed to be agreed on tactfully ig-
noring my silence. I decided to swallow the bitter pill of my
disappointment and show them, if not respect as conspirators,

then at least common politeness. I moved over to a chair beside the man by the window and started following the conversation without expecting much from it.

And as I listened I was filled first with confusion, then with a certain skeptical expectation and finally with a vague, indefinite hope. The Sunday trivialities were now exhausted and a sensible, intelligent exchange of thought was taking place. It was no longer the names of wines but the names of people I didn't know, who, I realized, had received help from this group in the way of food, money, clothes and transport. Then the conversation changed to the air raid of that morning. The people present were all surprisingly well-informed, each in his own field on the targets that had been hit. I made note of a few bits of information which I could still add to my report.

"Even my ward, usually reserved for venereal diseases, is packed with casualties from this morning," said the tall dark man rubbing a hand across his eyes. "Most of them were in a terrible state. And yet, we can do nothing but hope that the hammer will fall harder and harder in the months to come, even if we have to be the anvil. Rather take the jolt now and get it over, than having it continue over another year."

"If the 'Bannertrager' gets another year, there will be nothing left of Germany, not even enough to use as an anvil," the little fat man said. "He would rather see Germany in ruins than give up a single one of his insane notions. He is not fighting for anything but himself any longer. What he'd like best is to take us all with him into the grave."

"You can do a lot yourselves to prevent that," I found myself saying. "Why does an entire nation choose to commit suicide for the sake of one lunatic? Why not try to put the lunatic where he belongs?"

There was a short awkward pause. My neighbor looked at me inquisitively; the others exchanged embarrassed glances like people who don't quite know what to make of each other.

62

"It is difficult to get the lunatic certified, because unfortunately he happens to be head director of the asylum," said the dark man. "The most we, on the outside, can do, is to help each other now and then. Apart from that"—he pointed at the window—"the only help the Allies have sent us so far is bombs. If they should think one day of combining bombs with other less drastic measures, it is quite possible that we could give them a hand too," he added with a subtle smile.

The talk went on, about the duration of the war, the effects of the Western powers' entry into Berlin, unity among the Allies, Germany's exposed position in a no-man's land between two opposing views of life after the war. Later, while the naked facts of the general situation were slowly sifted from the motley material broadcast over the British and German radio, I studied the assembly more closely.

The first unpleasant impression I had received of the tall, dark doctor could hardly stand up against a more comprehensive study. The nervous gesture of his hand across his forehead, the deep furrows at the corners of his mouth and the simultaneously weary yet watchful look in the deep-set eyes, seemed to suggest a man who had been hunted for a long time and who sees a pursuer in every new face, rather than a sinister, gloomy misanthrope. The woman with the frivolous curl was still talking ten to the dozen, but flashes of wit added spice to everything she said. She was exceptionally well informed with regard to conditions in Scandinavia and revealed a bitter, sarcastic knowledge of the many greedy, dirty fingers in the German coal business, where, as far as I could understand, she had a job as a correspondence clerk. Maybe she was only talking so much because she was nervous, felt lonely and superfluous. Maybe she was just trying to drown out voices calling to her from the ruins of the three apartments which I learned she had been bombed out of.

The fat man with the glasses was having a quiet, semiprivate talk with the parson, who had long since dropped his professional manner. I gathered that the parson and his congregation had been persecuted and that it was still quite an act of heroism to be present at his sermons, but that one of those who still dared to do so was the little fat tanner of hides with the quiet voice and the easy sense of humor.

Eventually as these new characters made an impression on my mind, my uneasiness and disgust disappeared. I felt half ashamed of my behavior earlier in the evening. I ought really to be grateful for these contacts with some of the very few anti-Nazis in Berlin, who had done a bit more than just criticize the regime in the comparative safety of their own four walls.

"It is quite a pleasure to see new faces," I said almost enthusiastically to my neighbor. His coat collar was standing away from his neck, as if both he and his gray suit were suspended from an invisible coat hanger.

"So, you like this group?" he said. He added with his knowing smile, "Yes, it is a good thing to give yourself time to get to know people. I felt the same way the first time Carl asked me up here."

"You are new to the crowd, then?" I asked, embarrassed.

"Comparatively," he replied. "But they are all charming people. That is the amazing thing about Germans; when you get to know them, they are, like most other nations, made up of both—well, I'm not much good at lectures, nor listening to them for that matter. The only thing worth going by is what you have seen with your own eyes and experienced yourself. Shall we take a look?"

We walked together into the dark study, where he drew aside the black-out curtain. The sky was pitch black, but towards the east there was an inflamed reddish glow.

"There were quite a few divisions wiped out this morning," he said soberly. "This air attack will be felt both at the Rhine and the Oder. Incidentally it was felt here, too!" He pointed

64

to himself. "One of the bombs didn't know how to discriminate between friend and foe. It chose to fall near my factory out at Moabit. I trust it is not the teetotalers who have taken on the command of war operations."

The change was a bit too sudden and the possibility rather farfetched, but of course it couldn't do any harm to join him in hoping that such a catastrophe should not have befallen us.

"I hope not," I said seriously. "Rather a wet defeat than a dry victory."

There was a short pause. Then suddenly we both burst out laughing.

"You see," he said, "I have a liqueur factory out there. Fortunately I got away with a collapsed wall. You must come and visit me one day when you have nothing better to do."

The other guests were about to leave, when we returned, and I said good-bye to them and to the liqueur manufacturer. As the last, the doctor, moved towards the door, I grabbed hold of his arm. "Have you got a moment to spare?" I said. "There is something I'd like to talk to you about."

I had made my decision on the spot, drawn my number and hoped it would pay off.

We sat down by the low, round table in the study, where Carl and I had been sitting the night before.

"How about a drink?" I asked Carl, looking earnestly and questioningly at him. He caught on, nodded and went for the cognac. As he poured it out, no one said a word. I hesitated a moment over my glass, and then decided not to waste time beating around the bush.

"What would you say," I began, looking steadily into his dark eyes, "if I were to take you on your word? This evening, you said you might like to help the Allies if they gave you a hand. Here it is."

The doctor smiled faintly. "We didn't know in what shape you'd turn up, but we had a feeling you were coming. For months Carl has been talking of a foreign visitor we ought to cultivate a bit when he arrived. What can I do for you? Show you round the city?"

"I must try to establish several depots about the city as quietly as possible," I said holding his eyes. "At the same time, I am looking for billets for some of my friends who will be arriving——"

Carl interrupted us. "I thought maybe you could have a depot out in your house in Potsdam where you hid your wife those two days before we got her to Hamburg. . . ."

A deeper shadow passed over his already dark features. Apparently there was something he would rather not be reminded of. I poured him another drink which he drained right away.

"Naturally you need not make a decision tonight," I said. "Shall we meet here again Sunday night? And then you will tell me yes or no."

When he had gone I grabbed Carl by the arm. "For heaven's sake, have you told them who I am? Do all those people know why I've come?" I said excitedly.

Carl freed himself impatiently. "Take it easy, I'm not that stupid! Even if I don't sit sulking in a corner all night, weighed down by a deep and dark secret, I still know what's at stake, the risk I am running myself."

"I only meant," I said more calmly, "that we mustn't rush our fences; we've got to weigh our people one by one."

"I know everything about the people to whom I have mentioned you," Carl said. "I have known them for years. They realize what they are doing. All right then, let us take them one by one. Joseph, the doctor, for instance. Don't you think he knows the ropes? For the past twelve years he has been secretly married to a half-Jewish girl, living every single day for twelve years in the fear of being found out! He has moved her from place to place, kept her hidden. Don't you suppose he would do everything to be allowed to live the normal life of a human being? And the tanner from Bernau! You have no idea what that little man has done through his business connections in Switzerland. Or the parson! What wouldn't he do to get his church back and be allowed to say what he feels once more? I know what it does to his conscience to stand up there in his pulpit without reviling those who have mocked his faith."

Carl paused for a moment and sat down.

"Well—I just mean that they are people you can trust as surely as you trust me. What did you expect, anyway? A crowd of trained German saboteurs just waiting for the go-ahead from the big boss before they jump into action? No, my friend, you won't find anything like that here. We must take our material as it comes and where we can find it, right in the middle of everyday life and be grateful."

I said. "Please remember that these people, whatever they might be otherwise, are still Germans at heart. We are asking them to fight their own country. That's rather a lot to expect."

Carl pondered silently for a moment, as if he were trying to find words to express something complicated which only the initiated could understand. Finally he said,

"Either you believe it, or else you don't, but there are two kinds of Germans, each with his own idea of Germany as it is today. . . ."

I could not disagree with him. I had no experience to the contrary so far.

"What about the talkative lady?" I asked. "What do you know about her?"

"Heide? Only that twenty years ago she went to bed with some Swede and never got over it."

"And the quiet man who sat by the window?"

"I haven't known him very long, but he's on the level, too. He owns a liqueur factory. His name is Erikson. Makes good stuff, by the way. He's a queer bird. Always keeps outside looking on. I don't seem to be able to get the hang of him. I'm not very good at sitting around being silent with people. You'd better try to get an idea of him yourself."

"Does that go for the charming young lady you were so chummy with, too? Or do you find it easier to sit around in silence with her?"

"Lili!" Carl exclaimed, jumping up from his chair. "If you dare so much as approach her with your dirty leer! She is the sweetest, loveliest——"

"Save it," I said, waving him off. "I know all that. I'd rather you told me if she too knows who I am?"

"Of course she doesn't. As far as she's concerned, you're just one of my business associates. And that's the way you're going to stay!" He waved a threatening finger at me.

I suppressed a grin, for coming across the carpet was the usual procession: in the lead Uncle Otto, waddling along on his elbows, and Aunt Elfie following right on his tail.

They thought it was morning.

# chapter five

Early the next day I set about the difficult task of making my first contact with the courier system which was to transmit my reports to my chief and deliver to me future directives and equipment. For security reasons I was never told just how this system worked. All I ever learned was that there were a series of steps and alternative contacts along the way in case anything happened to some one of the persons responsible. In Berlin there were several different places for me to go in the hope of meeting one of the people whose descriptions I had memorized in Stockholm. If they responded to the code words I used during ordinary conversation I could pass over my coded report. I was to be ready at all times to pass to them a transmitter set should it be asked for by the methods prepared during my final briefing. In all work carried out by secret agents the prime precaution was observed: No one must ever know more than he needs to in order to perform his own task, so that if the worst befalls him he cannot be forced to tell what he doesn't know. This insures the safety of the largest possible number.

It was Tuesday morning, one of the three days a week when one of my courier contacts should show up some time between ten forty-five and ten minutes past noon at the church near Fehrbellinerplatz. I looked at my watch and realized that, if I walked directly there, I would reach the rendezvous well before eleven o'clock. I decided to go by a more circuitous route and arrive a little later.

When I found the church intact after the air raid of the previous morning I had a sense of great relief, knowing that I need not go in search of the next location on my list.

My pulse was beating much faster than usual. I felt as though anyone might see through my coat and recognize the innocent-looking report in an inner pocket.

Inside the church there were only a couple of elderly women kneeling in a dazed sort of fashion. I walked around as though interested in seeing if the walls of the structure had suffered any damage.

Suddenly I was aware that someone had come in by a side door. I did not look at once, but when I did, I was discouraged to see it was a small boy, who went quietly up to the two women and sat down beside them. After a few minutes all three got up and left.

I sat down in a back pew. A quarter of an hour passed. It seemed as though it must be late afternoon. Then a man entered. I did not look at him but felt him looking at me as he came and sat in the same pew. I glanced in his direction and saw a torn cloth glove on his left hand. So far so good!

I picked up a worn prayer book and muttered as if to myself, "Eighteen ninety-seven."

Straining my ears to catch any sound I heard him reply softly, "Nineteen hundred and two."

I looked around. There was no one in sight, so I reached into my pocket and drew out an old twenty-mark gold coin from the days of Kaiser Wilhelm I. Out of the corner of my eye I could see him doing the same. We each put one hand down on the bare wood of the pew, but cautiously so that the coins would make no sound as they touched the wood. As he raised his hand, I slipped mine over and picked up his coin. He deftly picked up mine. We each examined the exchanged coins. His was a twenty-mark gold piece bearing the numbers 1902. I calmly handed his back and took my own.

I sat for a moment, wondering if he had any message for me. When he did not move, I put my coin away and removed the report from my pocket. I picked up the prayer book again, opened it, slipped the report between two of its pages, closed it, and put it down on the seat between us. He made no move to pick up the book, and soon I got up to leave. I took a sharp look at him so that he would be photographed in my memory for the next time we met. As I moved away I saw him remove my report and place it in his pocket. I gave a last quick look around the church, offering my thanks for this little mission completed without mistake or trouble.

Coming back from this meeting, as I turned from Kurfurstendamm down our street—Cicerostrasse—I noticed a thick, woolly column of smoke as from a small explosion outside number eleven. Through it I could just make out the contours of a vehicle and a figure trying to get out of it. There could be no doubt that it was Carl and the Smoke Screen. I knew he made his own patent gasolene from various fluids and chemicals, which he brought home from his little factory, the ingredients, as far as I understood, being mainly ether, acetone and methanol combined with other refinements. I could see now that his invention was in fact a fluid more suited to sky-writing ads after the war, than a fuel which would take us round the city on our various errands without attracting undue attention. A brief glance at the museum piece behind the smoke convinced me that my decision to get rid of it must stand firm. I made up my mind to change the car and get some real gasolene.

"We're going out to the Kraftverkehrsamt," I told Carl. Kraftverkehrsamt was the motor and gasolene control office. He was struggling grimly with the engine.

He let the radiator hood fall with a look as if he were closing down the lid of a coffin.

"Does that mean——?"

"Yes, it does. You will have fourteen days to say good-bye to it while we use it to transport the supplies, because a van like this is best suited for that job. But after that it's the end. We might just as well fetch its funeral papers when we apply for some real gasolene. Will you run up and get the necessary things from the package we opened yesterday?"

He came back with a well-filled paper bag in his hand, slipped in behind the wheel and tried to start the engine. It responded with a hoarse rattle.

"Tell me, why haven't you ever offered Hitler your invention?" I asked, as I watched his complicated maneuvers.

The man behind the counter at the Kraftverkehrsamt polished his glasses on the sleeve of his shiny old alpaca coat and shook his head.

"The very existence of our firm is at stake," I told him. "I am responsible for bringing out the goods. Do you want me to push the van along?"

"All I can do for you is to renew your driving permit and give you permission to exchange your vehicle to buy another second hand car exempt from requisitioning," said the alpaca man patiently.

"But this is of great importance to the war effort," Carl said.

Idiot! I kicked his shin under the counter.

The war effort did not make the slightest impression on Alpaca Coat. With a weary gesture he pointed to a bookcase bulging with applications like ours.

72

Casually, I brought out the paper bag and placed it on the counter, leaning confidentially towards the man.

"We wouldn't trouble you, if it didn't mean so much to us. But in times like these everyone has to rely on mutual understanding and good will. . . ." With my elbow I gave the paper bag a tactful little shove towards him. The scent of coffee spread pleasantly over our little section of the counter. The alpaca man's nostrils quivered almost imperceptibly. ". . . . In such a situation it is one's patriotic duty to make the rules suit the current demands, don't you agree?"

He bent his head reflectively, letting my appeal sink into the utmost depths of his patriotic breast. Then he threw a quick glance at the paper bag, cleared his throat and started looking through our papers again.

"If you will make a statement to the effect that the gasolene will only be used for priority-one war purposes, there might be a possibility, under paragraph eighteen, of giving you a gasolene ration equal to the amount you have applied for," he said, addressing Carl.

Joseph, the doctor, turned up at the apartment at the appointed time Sunday night. Lili was walking around with averted eyes fixing the coffee table. She was still a bit embarrassed in my presence because of her position in the household. Uncle Otto and Aunt Elfie followed her until they collapsed from exhaustion at Carl's feet. It was plain that she wasn't a stranger to them at any rate, whether they thought it was night or morning.

Later, when Lili went to the kitchen to do the washing up, I looked questioningly at Joseph, but I had already read his answer in his face.

"It's okay," he said simply. "You can bring your supplies out tomorrow. I have prepared the place you mentioned, Carl. I had always hoped that room would never be used again. . . ."

His melancholy eyes stared into the blue smoke from his cigarette. He had had a haircut, which accentuated the long intellectual almost ascetic lines of his face.

"Lili! Bring us another drink," Carl called.

Lili appeared in the doorway, giving me her usual shy look.

"Aage is not as fierce as he looks," Carl said, beckoning her over. "But so many girls have given him the brush-off—that's why he's envious of others who are more fortunate."

"I think it's a shame they all ran away from you," she said, looking at me as a little girl looks at her favorite doll. "You don't seem fierce at all."

I sent Carl a triumphant look.

"He's clever at disguises," Carl said warningly but with a twinkle in his eye for me. "Next month he may have changed into a wolf."

"Nonsense!" Lili touched my arm lightly and pouted at Carl.

She left early, but the rest of us remained sitting with our drinks and planning the transport of the stores. Finally Joseph rose to leave, but as he stood in the hall with his hand on the doorknob, the sirens broke into their dismal wail and the ack-ack batteries fired a shattering volley.

"Mosquitoes," said Carl with a professional air, looking at his watch. "Punctual as an airliner. I don't feel much like going down into the cellar. What about you? Shall we have another drink? After all, we have something to celebrate tonight."

We went back into the room and Carl poured out the drinks.

The following day we started building up the depots around the city. We divided the supplies in the apartment into three more or less equal parts, so that if one hideaway was destroyed or discovered, we'd still have two others to fall back on.

Carl wore his oldest clothes and he lent me an ancient

74

overcoat and a cap with a broken visor. I got in behind the wheel of the Smoke Screen, pulled the broken visor rakishly over one eye the way I imagined a furniture remover would wear it and attempted to start the engine.

"What the hell! It won't move an inch," I said annoyed, stamping on the pedal. "You tell me it's a pre-Hitler model? Then it ought not to mind the kind of work we're doing today." I pulled out the choke. The only response from the engine was the familiar hoarse rattle.

Carl was sitting with his head on one side, apparently looking vacantly out through the windshield.

I gave him an impatient shove.

"Come on, do something! You're the inventor. We can't stay here all day, not with that load," I added nervously. "The stuff we have collected in the back qualifies each of us for at least a hundred firing squads."

Carl silenced me with an impatient gesture. He got out and started tinkering with the car. At length he stuck his head through the side window.

"I'm afraid I've put too much ether in the mixture," he said shamefacedly. "It's difficult to get exactly the right proportions."

The seriousness of the situation didn't prevent me from laughing. "No wonder the old thing is unconscious. Haven't you got something that will wake her up?" I said. Just then I caught sight of a uniformed person coming from our entrance. It wasn't an army uniform, but the Nazi Party dress, occasionally revealing all its silver-braided splendor under the long blue-gray coat, as the man without apparent hurry walked down the wide stone steps.

"Oh, God! That's the district leader," Carl whispered.

The Nazi lingered for a moment on the sidewalk, then he walked towards us with a smile. He raised his hand in a rather shoddy Hitler-salute, which Carl answered by tilting his crumpled hat.

"Won't it go?" asked the district leader in a deep and rather pleasant voice. "I've never seen you have trouble starting it, but from my window I've often admired your forced landings."

He laughed and bent over the radiator. "Shall I——"

"No, no," Carl murmured hastily. "We've just forgotten to put gasolene in her, but I have a can with a little drop up in the apartment. It'll take us to the nearest tank. I was just going to get it." He hurried up the steps.

The Nazi leader looked up and down the car a few minutes, like a man with time on his hands, and then shifted his eyes to me, still sitting behind the wheel with a completely irrational feeling of having been left in the lurch by Carl.

I managed to get my cap off without hitting the ceiling. The leader repeated his sloppy Hitler-salute and stepped closer. I got out of the car. I felt I could defend it better from the outside.

"It's not very often a car runs completely out of gasolene. As a rule there'll always be a drop left in the tank," I said, trying to lead the unavoidable small talk into neutral, technical channels.

The Nazi looked at me with interest. "One can hardly detect your accent," he said. "Are you a native German resident abroad?"

"No, I'm Danish," I said. "On a business visit to my friend here. We're going out to look at some samples at the factory. That's why we aren't exactly wearing our Sunday best."

He buttoned his coat. It was a stupid remark. And quite superfluous. What business of mine was it, if he could wear his Sunday best every day of the week?

"How's the general atmosphere up north?" he asked after an awkward little pause. He must have taken it for granted that I was on the right side. How would I have got permission to come to Berlin on business under the prevailing conditions if not in return for some service rendered?

76

I shrugged my shoulders hopelessly. "It's getting harder and harder for a businessman to make a living. People are going off their heads; you can hardly control them any more. All that beastly British propaganda! I wonder what would happen if the Wehrmacht dropped us one day. Communism and chaos! That's how it would all end."

Thank heaven international politics were still as simple as that! It would have been hard to express more original views, when my thoughts were centered on Carl's return.

"I expect you can still get everything up there," he said casually. "I mean meat and bacon, butter and bread? I wouldn't mind taking a trip up there to find out why they allow such a surplus in one spot, while the rest of Europe is spending its last reserves. . . ." Indignantly he stuck out his double chin and pushed his hands energetically into his coat pockets.

"The better part of the population up there are of course ready to make every sacrifice for the new Europe," I said, "but you know, mistaken patriotism. . . ."

Why the devil didn't Carl show up? My feet started tingling.

". . . . Allied propaganda, paid provocateurs, secret agents . . . it's all their fault that Denmark still has bacon and butter," I concluded feverishly—founding a brand-new and rather startling political school of thought—because I had just caught sight of Carl, coming out of the door with a can in one hand.

"This is what she needs!" he exclaimed, with infective confidence, walking round to the back of the van. The Nazi leaned lazily against the rear door to our stores. Carl's eyes, as he bent to unscrew the cover of the tank, were nowhere near as confident as his voice.

"Now let's see what she says to that," he said, getting behind the wheel. He turned the ignition key and stepped on the accelerator, at the same time fondling the choke. The Nazi stood with his hands in his pockets fascinatedly watching the inspired antics of the Wurlitzer-wonder.

77

A shock passed through the van, Carl and me, when the engine started abruptly with a violent splutter.

The Nazi stuck his head through the side window as Carl put the car in gear.

"Will your stay be of long duration?" he asked.

"Yes, some time yet," I answered vaguely.

"Then I'll pay you a visit at your friend's one day to hear some more about conditions up north. What you said sounded most interesting."

We drove for a while in silence, both too exhausted to speak. It didn't seem worth the trouble to ask Carl whether he agreed with me now that we would have to get another car. We headed towards Potsdam.

I finally broke the silence. "Who was he?"

"He's a district leader or something similarly brassy," Carl answered with a sigh. "And I wish he'd go to hell! I had hoped we would avoid him. He moved into the house this winter. It used to be such a nice house, but then the Party requisitioned the apartment on the first floor, and next day this fellow turned up. It seems that he had some big job in one of the eastern areas the Germans had to abandon. People say he's a great pal of Dr. Ley, who has given him some nice easy job on the Workers' Front, where most of the unemployed Nazis have got together. It's a front that suits them considerably better than the other kind. This fellow is probably scared stiff of having to change his fancy-dress uniform for a drab green battle dress. So he goes around making himself useful everywhere, pushing his nose into everything that doesn't concern him, just to prove that he's indispensable—on the soft and easy front. The people living in our house say that it's become a mania with him. You saw for yourself how he snooped around our car," Carl finished indignantly.

"Yes, as if there had been anything to snoop for," I said, sharing his indignation.

"But it sure was an unlucky coincidence," Carl sighed

again. "I've also frequently seen Gestapo officers visiting him. How did you keep him amused by the way?"

"He was most interested in the conditions in Denmark."

Carl laughed. "Oh, he was? Yes, I can quite believe that. He's been up to question me about Sweden, too. He's interested in all kinds of tourist information, probably because he's planning to do a vanishing act—with his girl-friend. He often brings a snappy number home with him. Can't understand a girl like that not looking for something with more future in it."

"Incidentally," I suddenly remembered, "what did you put in the can?"

"Spirits," he said innocently.

"Surely not our Swedish schnapps?" I asked in horror.

He flashed me an inscrutable look and started whistling.

Within two weeks the apartment was cleared to the extent that we only had the barest day-to-day necessities. We took the last parcels in a suitcase down to the Deutsche Union Bank, where we carefully placed them in Carl's safe-deposit box. He had never liked the manager, and as I didn't know anything favorable about this banker, I had no misgivings about depositing the last small batch of explosives in the security of his vault. At the same time the group that had met every week during the past two years for the purpose of hating was dissolved. I thought myself that their sentiments had been guided into more useful channels. None of them ever came to the apartment again, and it was kept in readiness for other visitors.

Carl had tracked down a garage, situated in a bombed East Berlin district where the ruins had been allowed to take care of themselves. Some of them, the results of the very first raids on Berlin, had even taken on a slightly mossy-green hue which indicated that Nature was in the process of recovering what man had taken from her. Carl drove the Smoke Screen along a narrow winding lane, finally running into an open area hidden by ruins on all sides. Some of the partly collapsed walls had been equipped with a temporary roof of charred boards and beams. Others had only a canopy of asphalt paper. Under one of these half a score of automobiles had been lined up.

A middle-aged German, wearing a short overcoat, came strolling out of a small shack in the center of the square. He nodded briefly in recognition to Carl and waited with his hands in his coat pockets.

"Is it one of those we're going to look at?" asked Carl.

The German pointed with a hand still in his pocket. "That one for instance."

I walked over to a Mercedes, shiny with new paint, and made a move to open the front hood.

Suddenly there was a spark of life in the German's eyes. He whipped his hand out of his pocket.

"Now then, no trifling with it! Take it as it is or leave it. There are plenty of others interested."

"Thirty-five hundred and fifty?"

The German seemed to have lost all interest. "Five thousand," he said in a weary tone.

I walked around the car kicking the tires. Heaven only knows how he'd managed to fix them up! On the face of it, it was quite a nice car. I supposed there was a possibility of its lasting the time out.

"Four thousand?" I suggested. The figure was a matter of complete indifference, but it was useful to get the feel of prices.

"You mean forty-five hundred," the German countered. "Is it liquid, grit or smoke?" None of us would have dreamt of mentioning German money.

Carl brought out my suitcase. "Mostly grit and smoke," I said, opening it. Then I suddenly remembered something and put it down again.

I walked over to the Mercedes and made sure that the red V—which meant that the car was exempt from requisitioning and could be used for private purposes—was painted on the license plates.

"I trust it's genuine?" I said.

The German gave a shrug. "It's there, as you can see."

"And the papers?" I asked.

He walked over to the shack and came back a moment later handing me an apparently brand-new set of papers. I started checking them off with the license number and general features of the car.

"You're wasting your time," he said. "Cheating wouldn't pay me in the long run."

I pushed the papers into my pocket and pointed at the Smoke Screen. "You'll take that as part payment?"

"Sure. Five hundred."

Carl's jaw dropped.

I opened the suitcase once more and started getting the things out. Two bottles of genuine cognac, which the German greeted with an expressionless glance; four pounds of coffee and two cartons of Chesterfields on which he bestowed a look that he tried to make expressionless. He reached for one of the bags with coffee.

"Now then," I said, "no trifling with it. There are quite a lot of people interested in grit, too."

I did not give him the four thousand in liquid, grit and smoke until he had backed out the Mercedes, and I was sitting behind the wheel.

I gave Carl a nudge in the side. He pulled the Smoke Screen's papers from his inside pocket and handed them through the window to the German. That was the last five hundred and, for Carl, the hardest to part with.

The German waved him off.

"Don't need them," he said indifferently like an artist who has no use for outside influences.

As I started up the engine I said to the German, "I'm pretty well fixed for grit and smoke, but I wouldn't mind handling a few side lines. So if you get customers here, who——"

"How much?" he interrupted.

"Ten per cent for you."

He nodded. "Come back in a couple of days."

In the weeks to come we were frequent visitors at the square among the ruins. The range of goods in the little ruin-shacks was new and surprising every time and showed us something of the inexhaustible supplies available on the black market. I had the pleasure of being introduced to a lot of hard-working businessmen who were just as interested in the Swede as he in them. I became a well-known figure on the square because my line, coffee and tobacco, had the highest rate of exchange.

It soon turned out that my guess had been right. The black market was in fact the shadow government of Berlin, upon which most Berlin folk depended, directly or indirectly, for the few luxuries that helped them face a new day. The market was as closely entwined with and as inseparable from the official government as a parasite clinging to its enfeebled host. The black market was the only reliable barometer which from day to day indicated not only the morale of the country but also its material situation. From the variations between supply and demand on this market, with its thousands of branches, I could, by using my common sense, work out—and even predict in my reports, certain measures taken by the Nazis both in Berlin and elsewhere.

The invisible threads of the black market stretched their network from district to district and soared upwards through all levels of army and party administration. Once you got hold of the main thread, it could lead you anywhere—maybe to the Workers' Front, maybe to the Air Ministry, maybe to one of the chief supply depots of the army. I followed every thread that looked promising and interesting.

"You've grown so strange since your friend came," I heard Lili say to Carl one day. She did not know that I was sitting in the study behind the half-open door making notes that marked the completion of a complicated deal, which included eggs from a wholesaler, a bale of cloth from a textiles man, some car batteries and radio spares from a top sergeant at one of the army depots and a carton of Chesterfields from me. My net takings were some radio spare parts and what turned out to be valuable information concerning the dispersing of some of the Nazi heavy-water experimental work which had been furiously carried on at Benemunde. I was anxious to get this report off as quickly as possible.

"You don't ever seem to do anything but eat and drink with those terrible people," Lili continued. "Where do you meet people like that, anyway? You never go to the factory any more. And why is Aage always writing letters home. If there's so much for him to do back there, why doesn't he go home and see to it himself? And a new car—you used to be so fond of the old one?"

I could almost see Carl taking her chin in his hand.

"Darling," he said. "Aage has a lot of business to do here. He knows a great many people. It may be true that they're not all equally nice, but one has to take business connections as they come. Anyway you've got to admit that he never lets us go short of anything. . . ."

"Well, I guess that's true," Lili answered hesitatingly. "It's queer, though; he's like two different persons, nice and considerate when we're alone, but nothing like that when you're in there with his friends. I see now why girls run away from him. No girl would put up with that very long." The last words were obviously a warning to Carl.

I bent reflectively over my notes. It wouldn't do for me to cause domestic disturbances. I had quite enough to handle already.

The weather became clearer every day, making the ruins stand out more vividly and the faces of the Berlin people seem more haggard. Spring was on the way, a renovation that seemed needless and almost paradoxical because it was taking place in a city moving with slow but unfailing certainty towards its doom. But just as people believe that others may die but never themselves, so the inhabitants of Berlin thought, during that budding spring of 1945 that, though Germany might possibly be destroyed, Berlin would always remain. I certainly had no idea that the end was approaching at a violent pace, and there probably was no one in Berlin, not even our secret depot managers, who in his wildest dreams saw the things that were soon to come. Maybe some had inward apprehensions, but they discarded them as too morbidly fantastic. Berlin was an island, whether in reality or in phantasy. The seas might pound its coast with raging surf, but wash across the island—never!

During this period I received a few directives in response to my reports so I knew they were getting through, but I got very little news as to the rapidly changing positions of the various armies.

Even as late as the middle of March the blood was still coursing through the countless veins of the great city, slowly and sluggishly, endowing the city with life. Every day the traffic system bore millions of Berlin folk from their ruined homes to their ruined places of work and back again, though breakdowns were more frequent and of longer duration. My eyes no longer saw the desolation around me, but just normal, everyday street scenes with twisted trolley tracks and mountains of rubble on the sidewalks. Like everyone else I got used to the fact that all shopping took place on the ground floor or one story below ground level in cellars where the windows had been replaced by thick stone or timber walls with a small open hatch facing the street. The mail delivery was normal, at any rate within the city limits, and papers were published daily always with the same contents—promises of new, miraculous weapons; rumors about a split among the Allies; exhortations to the weary not to be weary, to the dispirited not to be dispirited, to the wounded not to be wounded. There were still some restaurants open although their menus, with the exception of a few black-market establishments, were restricted to the coupon-free daily special: potatoes with gravy. You could still get a haircut and shave, have your shoes mended with some substitute or other, the liquid version of which probably served as beer; and you could, if you felt an urge to see rain, go to the movies and watch ancient worn films flicker over the screen.

In the meantime I gathered from the Allied broadcasting system that the Americans and British in the west and the Russians in the east were preparing their respective huge spring offensives. These waves would crash together in a last gigantic whirlpool right on Berlin, my center of activity. While I felt the excitement growing inside me, I began to realize that the life of a secret agent was not an unbroken series of nerve-racking adventures but a common, everyday job like all others, a medley of important things and trifles, disappointment and encouragement. Every morning I sorted out all the pieces of information on which I based my two or three weekly reports; in the afternoons we drove around building up the depots with the shipments that were still arriving by courier service, cultivated our contacts and saw to it that everything was being made ready for the day I was longing for more and more—the day when one of the couriers would bring me the message that the advance party of my contingent of trained saboteurs was on its way.

But there was still no message. Instead the medicine chest arrived.

"It looks very peaceful and innocent," Carl said, opening the two doors of the little rectangular chest. "It's just the kind of thing I've always wanted for my own bathroom, filled with a lot of funny little bottles and neat packages to look at while you're shaving."

He picked up one of the bottles but put it back immediately as if it burned his fingers.

"I suppose that isn't quite the kind of thing you had thought of putting in your pretty chest," I said, studying the bottle. "Poison tablets, preferably to be dissolved in coffee. Estimated time to elapse before lethal effect—seventy-five seconds. . . . Here's another one. You be careful of this. Dissolves in liquor. Works even faster."

Carl bent over the chest. "There are poison tablets for wine, too," he cried. "And absolutely tasteless," he added with relief. "There are still a few things which even scientists respect. . . . What's this for?" He picked out a miniature hypodermic from a collection of various other syringes and needles. "That's a pretty little thing for playing doctor."

"You may have heard of the Borgias," I said. "They always had their poison at hand, carried it in their rings. But science has made great progress since then. We have our little hypodermic in a coat pocket. The needle is protected by a small cap that will disappear when you press—there! When you need it, you just put your hand in your pocket, uncover the needle and make sure that its point protrudes between your fingers. Then you shake hands with the guy you don't like. If he doesn't like you either and you have to ward him off, just see that you do it with the hand that holds the needle. In either case he'll hardly feel the puncture, and anyway he'll have to be damn quick to complain—it works almost instantaneously. A neat and tidy method of causing an artificial stroke."

Carl stared with revulsion at the pernicious little weapon. "Are we supposed to carry them all the time?" he asked. "I don't like it. It's like having live snakes in your coat pocket." He gingerly replaced the hypodermic, and we passed on to less macabre contents of the chest.

There was a wide range of narcotics, also classified according to the fluids that would dissolve them. With their help we could put away an opponent from three to ten hours without having to kill him. In another compartment we found morphine and cocaine tablets. But nowhere was there an aspirin for a simple headache.

I had started practising amateur photography, but like all amateurs I was rather shy in public. The top sergeant at the army depot who had sold me various radio spares had become one of my best sources of information. Carl and I never questioned him or any of the others, we just baited them with some stupid remark or a completely ridiculous rumor, which they were only too eager to repudiate or confirm on the basis of their special, confidential knowledge. But the top sergeant was a rum character in every respect. Unsolicited he would tell us in his cynical jargon about everything that went on inside his own particular domain. He had worked his way up to a kind of Al Capone position at his depot, where he had the final say in the matter of how much each man was allowed to steal. He knew everything about everyone, right up to the colonel, and everyone stood in awe of him and loathed him intensely. He was the classic gangster, not without his own form of vicious humor but mainly possessed of a superiority complex, convinced of his own luck and invulnerability, a typical, self-assertive psychopath. When in the right mood he would reveal the most confidential secrets to me, deriving great satisfaction from my exclamations of feigned amazement—"No, you don't say?" "Is it really possible?" The exhibitionist enjoying the startling effect on others of his sudden exposures.

"They'll soon be changing their tune now, and we may even have an entirely new orchestra," this sergeant said one day as we were standing in the apartment listening to the thunder of the ack-ack guns during an air raid. "Do you know that they're setting up some new heavy guns around town? And all those fools thinking they're just reinforcement of the anti-aircraft barrage. No, sir, they're not that kind of gun. And they're going to be used for something quite different."

87

"What?" I asked innocently.

"Go and have a look at them yourself and make three guesses," he said.

I went straight out to one of the places he had told me about, but I needed only one guess. It was heavy artillery that could only serve one purpose: the defense of Berlin if the city were besieged. Germans hurried past the gun without looking at it, as if they purposely refrained from thinking about what its presence indicated. There was no barrier around it, only a lot of gunners and reserves bustling with activity. The clattering noise and the shouts of command from the gun emplacement completely drowned out the little click of the miniature camera in my palms as I pressed the plunger.

More and more of these new gun emplacements appeared, while at the same time the heavy ack-ack guns were frequently moved about. I tried, with the aid of my camera, to keep up with these comprehensive alterations for the defense of Berlin.

One evening after one of these fruitful days of photography Carl and I were sitting in the apartment over a bottle of cognac with the sergeant and another of our better-known connections, a dapper little textile merchant who, as a clever German businessman, was still cultivating his acquaintances among the high-up Nazis, while as a farsighted European his thoughts were also on the future, for which reason he had established a timorous contact with the remains of the twentieth-of-July opposition. The purpose of his visit that evening was to find out from me how he could best get his factory classified as neutral property, if—well, if the unthinkable (which nobody in Berlin believed) should happen after all. The sergeant was thoroughly enjoying the other man's flighty explanations and beating about the bush.

"Why not admit it outright?" said the sergeant contemptuously. "You're just as scared as my colonel was on the evening of the twentieth of July. But you know better than I do," he continued with a hard smile that made the textile merchant shrink against the back of the sofa. "No, if you want a bit of good advice from one who doesn't give a damn anyway, then you should do what I——"

What was it the textile merchant should do we never found out, for just then the doorbell rang, and Carl went out to open the door.

As bad luck would have it, our new guest was the district leader, making good his threat of paying us a visit. He was wearing a brown Party uniform without much adornment, presumably some kind of off-duty dress. He greeted everyone with an arm raised from the elbow. Carl and I nodded noncommittally, the textile merchant shot up from the sofa and gave a full-stretch Party salute, but the sergeant remained in his chair, lifting his hand carelessly. Carl pulled another chair up to the table and offered the Nazi a cognac.

"Well, how do you manage with your cleansing fluid?" the district leader began in a conversational tone, fondling his cognac glass and looking over it at me. "Isn't it a bit difficult to get chemicals at the moment? Of course that's the kind of thing you will get on a tight market," he said casually, as if the war were some annoying little bagatelle one had to put up with.

"I thought Mr. Schmidt dealt in textiles," blurted out the textile merchant from the corner of the sofa. Then he drew in his breath with a gasp, as if trying to draw the words back again. He realized at once that they were irrelevant and that outside the initiated circle such words were a decided evil.

But it was too late. It had happened. The district leader raised his eyebrows and looked inquisitively first at the textile merchant, who was still sitting with his lips puckered, then at me.

"But surely your main business is radio spares, is that not so, Mr. Schmidt?" said the sergeant. It was just like him, the sadist!

"The others are side lines," I said, trying with a sweep of my

89

hand to rid myself of troublesome cloth bales and annoying radio spares. "You've got to take everything that comes along. It's madness at a time like this to put all your eggs in one basket."

The sergeant sent the district leader an encouraging look and grinned maliciously. Why the hell did I always have to say the wrong thing in front of that Nazi leader? He moved restlessly in his chair and peered over at me.

"Of course my business is mainly chemicals," I declared firmly—much too firmly judging by the sergeant's eyes that sparkled with malevolent humor. "Come on, drink up," I said. "I think Carl will give us another bottle."

The leader kept looking at me, slowly turning his glass in his hands. Carl hurried out to get a new bottle. I thought of the poison chest, and the textile merchant undoubtedly thought of the twentieth of July. The sergeant was thoroughly enjoying himself.

The next cognac improved the atmosphere a bit. The district leader returned to our conversation of a few days before— about the conditions in Denmark. Accommodatingly I started on an extensive description of the little country in the throes of Allied propaganda, the distraught population and the misguided resistance movement. Here I was on more familiar ground than that of my own muddled business affairs. I warmed to the subject.

Finally the district leader interrupted me. "When we release our latest secret weapon, at the same time as the Western Powers realize that their alliance with Russia is treasonous to Europe's civilization and culture, Denmark and the other countries will soon come to their senses—again," he added, his thoughts probably wandering back to the great days of 1940. "Incidentally the army communiqué reported local advances on the Oder front this afternoon, and the commentary underlined the fact that this may well be the start of a decisive German offensive."

"In that case it's going to be a backward offensive," the sergeant interrupted. "They're piling up all the big guns here in Berlin. But, of course, you can interpret that in other ways, too" —he smiled to display ironic innocence—"that the Oder front is cluttered up with too many guns."

"It is the duty of every German to dispel his doubts," said the district leader. He stroked back his thick black hair, a gesture left over from bygone mass meetings when the applause had thundered towards him. "Our strongest and most secret weapon, because the enemy simply cannot understand it, is our faith in the Führer!"

The sergeant moved his lips in a silent amen. The twentieth-of-July man hung his head. Carl poured out the cognac once more—a big glass for the district leader—and everyone drank to whatever he happened to believe in.

The leader was getting a bit drunk. His eyes were bloodshot, the color of anchovies. He had some trouble getting them focussed on me.

"By the way," he said, "my radio has started making a terrible noise. Do you suppose it's because it wants new tubes? I'd like you to have a look at it sometime. If you're in the trade, you'll probably be able to see what's wrong right away."

I could tell by the sergeant's eyes that, if he were me, he would advise the district leader to give up listening to the British radio because it was always accompanied by a powerful jamming from some German station. I forestalled him.

"Certainly, if you'll take the risk," I smiled. "Even an expert can make a mess of it."

Had he taken up this awkward subject again on purpose?

The leader returned my smile. "Better to smash a tube or two"—I thought I saw him glance at Carl—"than let the whole apparatus go to ruin."

Half drunk, he chuckled into his glass as if he had just said something very subtle. If his remark was supposed to be funny, it could only be a private joke. Or did he mean something quite different?

"I'll come up and call for you one day and then we'll go over the radio together," he said raising his face from the glass. All his secret amusement had stayed down there. His features were loose and his skin full of large open pores. Once—maybe only a couple of years ago—it had been a strong face. New features had been slapped on over it, making it flabby and insignificant.

The conversation died out. Carl was sitting on the edge of his chair like a host ready to jump up and help the first guest on with his coat, but no one made a move to leave, mainly, I supposed, because there was nowhere better to go. When suddenly the sirens sounded to announce the arrival of the British Mosquitoes, I almost welcomed them as new guests.

The textile manufacturer, who was named Berger, jumped bewildered to his feet.

"That the all-clear? I'd better go then," he said, groping for his brief case.

The sergeant pushed him back in the corner of the sofa, where he instantly dozed again.

"Shall we retire to the cellar?" asked Carl hopefully, looking round the circle.

The district leader shifted in his seat and sent the sergeant a quizzical look which the latter returned with a contemptuous smile.

Carl shrugged his shoulders in resignation. "Then we had better have another cognac," he suggested.

The doorbell rang. Carl put the bottle down quickly and threw a look at the black-out curtains. Then he went outside to the hall. We heard him talking to someone and a moment later he returned, followed by a tall, slender girl dressed in a tight-fitting black coat with a collar of Persian lamb. She stopped in the doorway and inclined her head in greeting while her eyes wandered round the room with an appraising look. Then she walked with quick, sure steps over to the district leader, who lay back in his chair straddling his legs in front of him.

Suddenly he came to life. For a brief moment he looked

with annoyance and reproach at his hands, which were both occupied—one holding the cognac glass, the other a cigarette with the long ash still on it. Then pressing his elbows against the arms of the chair he made a laborious attempt at getting upright. The girl followed his exertions without showing the slightest feeling, which I for some reason interpreted as yet another criticism.

"Here are the papers, ready for your signature," she said handing him a zippered brief case. It was made of pigskin and had an elaborate monogram in one corner.

"Excuse me, gentlemen," he said in a thick voice, meanwhile dropping the cigarette ash on the brief case. "I have to move my office with me. But when you're on duty twenty-four hours a day. . . . By the way, how did you know that you would find me here?" he asked the girl.

"It was the last thing you told me before going to lunch," she answered sweetly. The sergeant grinned and flashed her a look of approval. The district leader made a face that was supposed to simulate importance as he drew the papers from the brief case and spread them out in his lap.

"You're working late?" I said to the young girl and offered her a seat in the armchair by the window. I felt rather unsure of myself. She was the cool, confident type that always made me nervous.

She started tapping her well-shaped foot, encased in a thin black shoe without straps, and tilted her head slightly looking up at me.

"Everyone in Berlin does," she said with an ironic smile, nodding her head almost imperceptibly towards the center of the room. "It's a matter of getting our files up to date before they are burned. What the hell does it matter, anyway! Can't see why they bother!"

It was the sergeant's language, the language of more and more people in Berlin.

"What you've just said, Fraulein—isn't that what is commonly called defeatism?" I asked in an effort to take up the uneven fight. Incidentally she looked far less impressive sitting there curled up in the chair. "Supposing I reported you? I think I've heard that you can get a severe reprimand and even a fine for that kind of thing."

"You wouldn't do that," she answered teasingly. "You're a suspicious character yourself. All foreigners are now, at the eleventh hour. And anyway, nobody would dare try and find out where a little secretary gets her defeatist ideas. Supposing it was disclosed that she had overheard them, when her employer had forgotten for a moment that she was in the room."

"How do you know that I am a foreigner?" I asked.

She nodded towards the district leader who was juggling with the cognac glass, fountain pen, cigarette and documents at the same time.

"And how do you know that I am a suspicious character?" I asked in a voice which I hoped was sufficiently casual.

She answered with the same bantering smile as before and a shrug of her shoulders.

I brought her a glass of cognac and offered her a cigarette. Her fingers were long and supple and tapered into curved nails of a dull red. There was an exclusive and expensive look about her. I wondered whether she was State or private property.

I raised my glass. She returned my greeting with a slanting look under her raised eyebrows. They had been strongly pencilled, almost too strongly. Maybe that made her appear more arrogant than she really was.

"I always enjoy meeting foreigners," she said. "Just the faintest little accent, just another kind of tie, a different cigarette. . . . It's so refreshingly new, exciting, secretive. And when your horizon has become limited to the distance between Fehrbellinerplatz and Brandenburger Tor you have to meet excitement halfway if you don't want to miss it. Incidentally I've always found suspicious foreigners the most exciting of all."

"Good heavens, Fraulein, I'm just another dull businessman," I said. "There's no excitement whatever in me. Why do you keep saying that I'm——"

"I might tell you some other day," she said in a low voice as she got up.

I turned in my half-seated position on the arm of the chair. Carl was rocking on the edge of his chair listening with a stiff polite smile to some sarcastic comment from the sergeant. My eyes wandered over the table with its full ashtrays and wet rings from the glasses. From there they wandered right into the red-rimmed eyes of the district leader. I had a nasty feeling that he had been sitting there the whole time watching my slightest move.

"Tell me, Mr. Schmidt," he said with the sly cunning of the inebriated, "you must know a lot of our people in Copenhagen? What has become of Obergruppenführer Schruber? You're sure to know him."

"By name only. I've never had the chance of meeting him," I answered hesitatingly and stared reflectively at the floor. I didn't want to catch the sergeant's or the young girl's eye.

The district leader mentioned another of his real or imaginary friends. I knew him by name, too. It would have been dangerous to imply more. I tried to look even more reflective. The firing had stopped outside, but that only served to make the silence of the room more deafening.

"Surely you know someone? Who, for instance?" the leader persisted.

"For instance, Dr. Best, the German High Commissioner in Denmark," I answered casually. "He is one of my personal friends."

"Is that so?" exclaimed the district leader rising halfway to his feet with feigned respect. "I had no idea you moved in such high circles." It was quite obvious that he didn't believe me.

"Well, I do," I said sharply.

I pulled Dr. Best's letter of recommendation from my

pocket and flung it at him. At the same time I realized how ridiculous it was to get angry because someone doubted the existence of my high-up Nazi connections.

The district leader did not seem nearly as drunk as before. He examined the letterhead meticulously and started reading the contents.

"Do you mind if I leave now?" asked the young girl and moved towards the door.

The leader rose to his feet and started to follow her, hurriedly scanning the last lines of my letter.

He gave it back to me in the hall.

"And we'll look at the radio together some evening, shall we?" he said.

In the dim light I couldn't see whether he was still drunk or nearly sober, nor could I tell from his voice whether to regard his words as a threat or as an attempt to make excuses for his behavior.

"Wait a moment," he said to his secretary, who was already on her way down the stairs. "Let me see you down."

I decided that I couldn't be bothered to wait and make sure that the street door opened and closed, so I went back into the room, still straining my ears towards the staircase.

"This wasn't one of your more successful evenings," said Carl reflectively later. "Now he's got something to take an interest in. Why the hell does a creature like that have to go and get unemployed?"

"It can't all run smoothly," I said. "Fortunately I know more or less from our own sets how a radio is put together. But I'm not keen on the idea of playing mechanic at his place. And we've got absolutely nothing on him, if the worst should come, have we? What was it you called it? Ordinary German reinsurance?"

"Only that he seems to be keeping that snappy dish we've just seen. And that kind of thing hasn't got anyone in trouble with the Party yet."

"Nonsense!" I said indignantly. "She's much too smart to touch that inflated uniform."

"One generally gets around to touching several things, when there's nothing else to hang on to," Carl stated philosophically. "I only hope the little secretary won't disturb the boss's sleep tonight."

# chapter six

The following day I received a message through the couriers that two of my men were at last on the way, an explosives expert and a specially trained radio man. They would be arriving at the tank station in Bergedorf one of the first days of April. There was no time to lose. We started making counterfeit traveling-permits both for ourselves and for the other two agents in case of emergency. We were happy to know that things were beginning to hum. The atmosphere in the apartment after the district leader's visit and his badly concealed threats had been both tense and nervous. Carl and I had moved into the same bedroom. We did not undress when we went to bed, and we always had our guns ready within reach. The slightest thing, an unfortunate coincidence, an innocent slip of the tongue could be fatal. Without being unduly dramatic we agreed to try and shoot our way through if anything should happen, and, if that didn't work, to turn the guns on ourselves. Neither of us had much confidence in the medicine chest.

Lili came to the apartment as usual. She was sweet and charming as ever, but even if Carl refused to admit it, she added to the complexity of the situation. She never said much, but I could understand that she made her observations and had started wondering. She was another problem that had to be dealt with. And still I hadn't found another place to which I could move and yet be in control of the whole show.

On the afternoon of our departure for Hamburg we decided to make certain alterations in our papers to give the entire expedition a semi-diplomatic appearance. Practically all traffic between the two cities had ceased. Two ordinary motorists might attract considerable unwanted attention. We spent the rest of the afternoon with a jigsaw and a pot of paint and when we had finished we had the most splendid C.D. plate for our Mercedes. We put on our best clothes and our most discreet ties in order to represent the country, in whose interests we were traveling—Sweden—in a correct and dignified manner.

We set off around eight P.M. and drove west through Potsdam, where we stopped at Joseph's house to have a quick look at the depot. Unfortunately he was not at home. We used our own key and found to our pleasure that our main arsenal was in perfect condition just ready for use. Then we continued northwest until we were a good way out of Potsdam on the road to Nauen. There we heard the sirens wailing over Potsdam and shortly afterwards there was a steady drone high in the air above us. When we saw the "Christmas trees," the hovering red flares that marked the target, we ran the car down a forest lane and got out.

The attack which laid Potsdam in ruins started then and there with a violence that made us fling ourselves to the ground.

The air vibrated with enormous explosions and the sky above the city was slashed by terrible jagged flames. Concussions were so terrific that I grabbed a stick between my teeth to prevent them breaking and pressed my cheek against a moss-grown stone.

I thought of our arsenal. We had rejoiced only half an hour ago because it was safe. It would now be adding its tiny voice to this thunderous doomsday orchestra. Were we playing our small part in painting red the skies over Potsdam? I compared my daily efforts during the past six months with these giant forces that started as a quiet hum and ended with a roaring crash that made the bones of one's face vibrate.

I experienced a chaotic feeling of frustration, reverence and envy, but above all a suffocating impotence.

During a lull in the attack we jumped into the car and drove madly on. The night was pitch-black. It was almost impossible to see the road in the dim glow of our blacked-out head lamps. I shall never know how we managed to escape from that roaring hell behind us. I wondered if Joseph had been lucky enough not to get home before it started?

In another hour of crazy driving we reached the control post outside Perleberg. Our diplomatic papers were accepted without question, but the gendarmes firmly ordered us to extinguish all lights including the narrow slits in the head lamps.

"How do you expect us to get on like that?" asked Carl with a Swedish accent I had never heard before. "The darkness is like a wall around us. We are on a highly important mission and we've got to get there quickly."

"If you're all that busy, then shut off those bloody lights," the gendarme said irritatedly. "The sooner you do that, the more time you will save. It's the same for everyone now," he added maliciously.

It was a different reception from the one I had encountered two months before.

We could do nothing but comply with his insane demands, and we started sneaking along through Perleberg in total darkness. I was concentrating hard on driving, but we had gone only a short distance, when I experienced an unpleasant apprehension.

"Try getting out a moment," I said slowing down.

"There's something so queer. . . ." I peered into the darkness, but couldn't see a thing.

Carl opened the door and got out, while I went on at a slow pace.

"You're quite right," he said. "It's a queer kind of street. It slants so steeply you can hardly keep your balance. You're sure we haven't strayed up on some roofs? The paving is as slippery as tiles."

Suddenly I felt him grabbing hold of the door. "Stop, for God's sake, stop! We're heading right for the canal!"

I gave him my handkerchief and asked him to walk in front. In that way we managed to get through the town and back on the highway to Hamburg. Carl jumped back in his seat and I switched on the lights again. They weren't much help, but at least I could make out the road as a faint gray blur in the midst of all the blackness.

"There's a guy who doesn't give a damn for any gendarme," said Carl when a strong beam of light came over a hill in front of us. "I wish he'd take it easy so that we could have some benefit from all that light."

There was no need to worry. He did take it easy. It was an ammunition truck standing ablaze in the middle of the road. It must have been burning quite a while, but it was still lighting up the whole countryside.

"Maybe after all it is a good idea not to carry too much light this evening," I said. "What do you think of that?"

Quickly I averted my eyes from the wreck of another Mercedes that lay smoking up against the ammunition truck. A blackened object was dangling out of the twisted window frame. In the gleam from the burning ammunition truck it shone brightly black, as if it had just been tarred. It was shaped like the shrunken arms and shoulders of a dwarf.

"That's the trouble with that model Mercedes," I said. "It has the gasolene tank in front. Maybe we should have thought of that before we bought this thing."

"Yes, and the trouble with those humming birds up above is that they haven't really got the time to worry about C.D. plates," Carl philosophized pessimistically. "You'd better shut off the lights again."

Later on we passed a seemingly endless tank convoy moving east. The tanks loomed out of the darkness like huge, gray prehistoric monsters. As far as we could see, they were joined up in pairs, one towing another. An instructive picture of the current gasolene situation, which I would certainly include in my next report. In front of each pair of tanks walked a soldier, with a white armlet, showing the way.

On a long stretch between two hills the darkness closed in completely, and I had to drive entirely by the sound of the tanks, passing barely half a yard to the side of us. I shall never forget the sound that kept coming out of the black nothingness, the faint rattling, muffled by the night—caterpillar tracks against the surface of a road that seemed much too narrow to hold both this mechanized ghost train and our little car.

We were still so shaken by the blasting of Potsdam and by the strain of blind driving that our senses were incapable of registering our exhaustion.

As it got lighter, the highway came to life. From side roads and forest glades new tanks and ammunition trucks appeared, as well as trucks loaded to the brim with soldiers. But it was difficult to say whether the moving vehicles outnumbered the shattered units, abandoned at the side of the road.

Now a strange trail appeared in the fields along the roadside—one horse carcass after the other, some battered beyond recognition, rider and horse in one shapeless mass, others seemingly unscathed as if they had dropped dead from sheer exhaustion. The trail of dead horses led us to a railway crossing where the barriers were lowered. There we met the last remnants of what had once been a Hungarian cavalry division. The squat Hungarian farmer lads, dressed in tattered dirty uniforms, sat in their saddles with a miserable, lost expression on their faces, trying to control the nervous horses that reared and whinnied as a train rolled past.

When I came into the little concrete hut at the tank station at Bergedorf, the old man aged far beyond his years by concentration camps, was sitting by the table alone. He was dressed in greasy dungarees like the ones his son had been wearing two months before. There was a brief light of recognition in his glassy eyes, as I gave him my hand.

"Anyone been here asking for me?" I inquired expectantly. The old man shook his head.

"Are you quite sure? I persisted. "There should have been two men yesterday. Maybe your son——"

"They've taken my son," said the old man tonelessly. "I sit here all day. There has been no one."

As I stood beside him I was aware of a growing depression, which I felt could be understood by this man, old before his time, but words were superfluous.

"Will you send my regards to Evald? He's still on the run, I suppose?"

The old man nodded absently. It was an affirmative as well as good-bye. As I moved towards the door I had an increasing realization that the best-laid plans may often be taken out of men's hands.

We drove back along some smaller roads to the north, because we had reckoned on getting along faster in this way, but we only managed to get mixed up in a still greater chaos than on the way out. This time it was not a matter of scattered army units on the march but of whole German villages evacuating from the east. For the first time we saw dead bodies of civilians, a great many of them, all those who had not been able to keep up but had fallen dead from hunger or exhaustion.

Carl drove the car, but his eyes were fixed on the dead lying in the fields along the road. An old man had collapsed right next to the carcass of a cow, its swollen belly the blue-black color of those bed bolsters I remembered from my childhood in the country. The old man lay face down in the plowed field with his hands stretched out in front of him as if he were reaching for the inflated bolster.

"The bloody thing about war is that it's so unimaginative and it makes people unimaginative too," said Carl gloomily. "War dulls the senses; you lose the ability to get indignant, to protest, because it all becomes so interminable and impersonal. Finally you just regard it as one big railway accident that was nobody's fault. By now all those bodies look exactly alike to me, but take the old guy in there with his face in the dirt. He was a real living being once, too. He was a kid at play. A young man in love, laying great plans for the future. A mature man with wife and family. Now he should be sitting under the old chestnut tree on that farm playing with his grandchildren in the afternoon sun. Instead he's lying there, reaching out ridiculously for that inflated carcass. It's not decent, it's immoral."

We got stuck on the end of a long column of armored cars. Carl tried to pass them but was waved back by the irritable drivers. He slowed down and dropped back still farther. "I have a feeling," he said, "that if you can't get by, it will be best to keep them at a distance."

That feeling saved our lives. . . . Without the slightest warning there came a roar from the skies, and it seemed that a giant hand suddenly swerved the car aside. Carl jerked the wheel over to the right and we both flung ourselves out, each to his own side. Before I drew my head down into the ditch, I noticed that the small section of the horizon which I had time to see was streaked with slanting, gray-white stripes. At the same time I heard a seething hiss. The giant hand came back pressing me violently into the ditch. A scorching heat engulfed me.

Time passed by. I remained lying in the ditch. The giant and the roar disappeared, but the heat increased. I raised my head cautiously and looked across the road. There I saw Carl's ash-blond hair slowly coming into view.

"Are you all right?" I called. He put a hand behind his ear with an expression of strained listening.

I ran over to him and repeated my question.

"I shall be, when I've let all those roars out." He jabbed a finger round inside his ear. "Rocket fighters, weren't they? That's the nastiest experience I've had yet."

Simultaneously we turned our eyes towards the car. It seemed to be undamaged. Then we looked in the direction from which the scorching heat came. The German convoy had stopped in the middle of the road neatly dispersed at regular intervals. Only there were no vehicles any more, just the white-hot contours of the steel constructions. The heat was so intense that we dared not drive past this flickering neon picture of total destruction. We turned the car, found a new side road and zigzagged our way along towards Berlin. Neither of us spoke. We thought of our arsenal in bombed Potsdam, of the two agents who had not arrived and of the unmistakable signs of collapse we had seen along the roads. The end could not be far off.

The following morning when Lili came to the apartment she told me acidly, "A woman phoned you yesterday. A woman with a voice you could literally pour out of the receiver. You were to call her at this number. She said it was urgent."

I looked at the slip of paper. The number didn't mean anything to me.

When Lili had left, I said, "I have a feeling it will be the little secretary. It'll be interesting to see what we can get from her."

"Or she out of you," Carl replied soberly. "Supposing it's a trap?"

"There was something she wanted to tell me. What I don't know is whether she just wants to make a deal."

"Make a deal? With what?" asked Carl.

"I'll probably know tonight. She's looking for her way out.

Whatever her motive might be, I have a feeling that she may be willing to show us around backstage."

I put down my coffee cup and got to my feet.

"By the way, don't worry if you don't see any more of me today. I must get fixed up with another apartment. Get everything ready for a quick retreat if it should be necessary. Move everything suspicious out of here and take it to the depots. Be careful. I'm not sure your Legation can save your hide, if you get caught. And another thing. Can you trust Lili implicitly? Is she sufficiently grown up?"

Carl nodded. "Enough for me to marry her as soon as all this is over."

"Good, then tell her a little of what we're doing. But only so much that she won't give the wrong answers and get mixed up in something if they start questioning her and she tries to cover up for us."

I could see how relieved he felt. "Anything else?" he asked.

"Yes, run out to Potsdam and see what's happened to Joseph and the depot."

"Shall I wait up for you tonight?" he asked.

"You can discuss that with Lili," I replied.

Erikson's liqueur factory at Moabit was bigger than I had expected and the products were excellent, pure ingredients and marvelous recipes.

"There has been a sudden step-up in our production," said the owner with his quiet smile, laying a gentle hand on one of the wooden casks in a long hall, where there was a spicy smell of old oak and mystical essences.

"Early this morning some Gestapo people showed up. They made me swear to all kinds of secrecy before they told me that the entire production should go to the eastern camps—you know the huge camps with Russian and Polish slave laborers. You see that order tells more than all the army communiqués put together! When Gestapo starts dishing out liqueur to its slave laborers it can only mean one thing—that the slaves will be masters in a very short while."

"Do you think the end is as near as all that?" I asked.

He made an impatient gesture as if others before me had bothered him with the same stupid question.

"I've ceased working with notions like beginning and end," he said. "It's all one continuous rolling of waves, where one wave drops its flotsam onto the next."

He smiled and fingered a small bottle for a moment before he went on almost shyly, "I've often thought that the history of mankind is like the story of one man who keeps washing his hands but never can get them clean because they are black from birth. Maybe that's something I've read. . . . Anyway, that wasn't what you came to talk about. Try tasting this one." He handed me the bottle and a small glass. "I've taken great trouble so that they'd have something really good to celebrate their liberation from those camps."

When I took his hand before leaving, I said casually, "By the way, there's something I want to ask you. I can't go on taking advantage of Carl's hospitality, so I am looking for a small apartment or a couple of rooms. In quiet surroundings, as they call it. You don't happen to know of a place? I don't mind telling you that I——"

He cut me short. "You don't have to tell me anything. I'd rather not hear about your business. In these times it is an advantage to know as little as possible about each other. But if I can do you a personal favor, I shall be pleased. Should you suddenly find yourself without a roof over your head, come to me." He wrote an address on a scrap of paper. "I'll fix you up some way."

Her name was Ruth. She lived just off Fasanenstrasse in the half of a house that was still standing. Her environment was like herself, marked by good taste and a discreet, rather cool elegance. The furniture was light and airy, modern and chosen with a sure eye for line and color. Only the huge radio-phonograph seemed out of place, like an automobile that had crashed through the wall with its flashy chromium front and had stuck there. I don't know why, but it made me think of her slightly exaggerated eyebrows and too bold red nails.

On a small table there was a photograph in a silver frame. It resembled the district leader, but it was a younger, healthier-looking, dark fellow in uniform.

She followed my glance. "Funny, it's the first thing everyone who comes in here looks at," she said. "But I'm going to let him stay. He belonged here once."

"I can only respect you for that," I said. "But do such a lot of people come here? You sound as if it were a main thoroughfare."

Smiling, she moved the young man in his silver frame over to the sideboard and put a small cloth on the table.

"You speak like my old aunt. Of course people come here. Where else could one meet? By the Gedachtnis church, and go for walks in the moonlight admiring the ruins? But just think how shocking: people often spend the night here too! Are you sure you aren't ashamed to be sitting here at all?"

She changed to another tone. "It is the only sensible thing the war has done. It has proved that everything we found so important before—what you could do and what you couldn't—that all those things are ridiculous trifles and even less if that's possible. The most unimportant thing in this world is where you sleep——"

"Or with whom?" I inserted.

She tilted her head to one side and threw an appraising glance at the little meal on the table, French sardines in a tin and toasted bread. Then she walked over to the sideboard fetching a decanter.

"That is up to yourself," she said lightly, "though I admit that as a general rule, even that is not very important—any more."

She motioned me to a seat at the table. She was an accomplished hostess, even if she did claim a contempt of formalities.

"What is important then?" I asked.

She sat for a while with lowered head, twisting her wineglass in her fingers. Then she raised the glass and nodded at me with her little ironical smile. "To set the stage," she said, once more looking down at the glass as if she found inspiration in it. "Kid yourself into believing that everything is the way it was. Twist in front of the mirror in your new spring costume. Visit a sidewalk café on Kurfurstendamm, have dinner at Hotel Eden or Adlon. Then visit the all-night bars. See the smart uniforms around you, both inside and out of the silver frame. Feel like a woman, know you are desired. . . ." She threw back her head defiantly. "That's important! Refusing to believe that those things are over—that's important!"

Her hand shook slightly. We drained our glasses. It was a wine of a good year with a soft, spicy aftertaste.

There was a short pause.

"I like your face," she said finally, quite composed once more. "I love studying faces and trying to guess what's hiding behind them."

"What do you see in mine then?" I asked.

"At the moment nervousness, maybe even a slight feeling of uncertainty."

"And behind the uncertainty?"

"I don't know yet. That's the exciting part of it. Your friend the district leader seems to think so, too. In fact he is so excited that he has sent an inquiry to Denmark to find out who this Herr Schmidt can be, with his letter of recommendation from the German High Commissioner, what services he can have rendered him and what his business is here."

I lifted the wineglass and studied its intwined initials. "He could have saved his energy for a more useful purpose. My papers are in order and my business here is strictly legal."

"He has also sent an inquiry to the border post as to when, and by what means of transport Herr Schmidt crossed the border."

"How do you know all this?"

"Because I have written the inquiries myself."

"And why do you tell me about it?"

She leaned back in her chair, playing absent-mindedly with the knife on her plate. Then she bent towards me suddenly and exclaimed with a shrill note in her voice, "Why? Do I know why myself? Maybe because I've been made a fool of and want to get my own back. Maybe because my nerves can't stand any more. Maybe because I, as you believe, am trying to find a way out of the whole mess with the help of the first foreigner who happens to come along. . . ."

She laughed cynically.

"In the office today they were talking about a speech Goebbels made to his staff yesterday, something about showing a Technicolor movie in a hundred years' time about these days we are living through now. We'd all have a chance to get a part in it if we knew how to act as German heroes and heroines now. In a hundred years' time the audience would admire our heroic death struggle and come out from the epic film deeply moved. Just imagine, he said we would all be brought back to life a hundred years hence. . . ."

There was a touch of hysteria in her voice, as she went on. "A hundred years hence! Be brought back to life! Like a painted shadow on a white screen! No, I want to live now! Oh, I don't give a damn if they shout and boo at me in a hundred years' time. I'm here now. I don't want to be part of a death struggle. They're crazy, mad, insane. . . ."

She paused in an effort to control herself.

"But I'm only one of the extras in the supercolossal Agfacolor, 'The Fall of Berlin,' she continued, no longer hysterical, but with bitter sarcasm. "There are plenty of us, so the producers don't have to save on the crowd scenes. But what about the stars in the movie? Are they putting on their make-up for the last great scene on the barricades? I know a couple who are getting ready, the leader of the Workers' Front, Dr. Ley, and his press manager. They have fled from their offices to a private apartment somewhere in the city. There they are preparing for their last heroic appearance behind the last barricade—of bottles."

"I thought you were the district leader's secretary," I said to lead the conversation into more concrete channels.

"I was secretary to Ley's press manager before the two gentlemen retired to private life," she answered. "The worst thing that can happen these days is to find yourself without a boss. That means the ammunition factories or service on the anti-aircraft batteries, and my hands are not exactly suited for it. That's why I managed to get three bosses, two in the private apartment and their drinking pal at the office. Can you think of anything more ridiculous," she went on, "than to move heaven and earth to get you out of the way, when they'll be going down the drain themselves in two weeks. How unimportant it is!"

I leaned across the table and put my hand over hers. "Not for me. Will you let me know if there are more—misunderstandings—in my case?"

"And what can you do for me?"

So she wanted to bargain! It was just as I had thought. But obviously here was a valuable source of information.

"Plenty," I said with real emphasis, "if you are prepared to keep me informed. Do you think you can rely on me?"

She returned a steady gaze in which I detected a glimmering of hope. "Yes," she replied simply.

Some days later as I went in to breakfast I was greeted with an entirely new look from Lili.

"'Morning," she said businesslike, trying to conceal her

overwhelming excitement. "There's a man who has been phoning you all morning. Carl has a message for you. The depot at Potsdam blew up during the air raid, but Joseph wasn't there at the time," she added professionally.

We exchanged a conspiratorial look after which I went to join Carl in the study.

"It's Berger, the textile man," he said. "He claims to have got hold of some important information. But he won't part with it unless we give him a poster, so I suppose we had better let him have one. I'm not quite happy about that," he frowned. "After all it wasn't meant for that purpose, but as everyone with a bad conscience would say, 'As long as the intention is good. . . .' "

We both looked at the little poster at the top of which there was the colored flag of a neutral state and beneath it the information, printed in English, German and Russian, that wherever this poster was hung one would be on the property of the neutral country in question.

"God knows how much good this poster will do," I said skeptically. "In wartime people don't usually respect No Admittance signs. Can all Russians read, do you suppose?"

"It would certainly be nice to know," said Carl reflectively. "I wonder what they're like. In Berlin they only know Goebbels's Russians, who as you know are a lower and still not fully developed species of gorilla. There was general panic at the barbershop this morning. The Russians have started a terrific offensive on the Oder front, to which Hitler has replied with a terrific declaration assuring us that Bolshevism will share the eternal fate of Asia and collapse before the German capital. That's why a lot of Berlin people are already fleeing westward. So now it is about to happen—what everyone refused to face. I have a feeling it's not going to be too pleasant." He bent over the other posters lying in the desk drawer. "Yes, I sure hope the Russians can read!"

"Where do I meet Berger?" I asked a bit impatiently, but

then I remembered that Carl in his own way had belonged to Berlin for a long time. I took his arm. "I know what you mean. In a way it is your city, too. But we must take everything in the order it comes. All right then, what did he say?"

A few minutes before four o'clock I sauntered past the gutted church, which we could see from our windows, and once more I decided that it probably looked a lot better as a ruin than it had when it was still intact. I crossed the square in front of it and stood for a moment looking at the little park. I had completely forgotten that it was spring, and now that I suddenly saw it, I almost gasped with delight. Bushes and trees had budded with the faintest and most delicate, light green. Everything was neat and airy, delicate and beautiful as if it had all been brought to life by a soft breath and could disappear again if someone broke the spell with a misplaced remark, raucous laughter or a too sudden movement.

I pulled a newspaper out of my pocket and stuck it under my arm, looked at my watch and went into the circular building opposite the park. Inside there was the same smell that you find in all other public lavatories all over the world, but I couldn't stop a profane thought from entering my head—that the circular building looked exactly like the cupola of the gutted church, as if some thoughtful giant had lifted the lid off the church on the night of the fire and set it down here for the benefit of those taken short.

I was alone as I had expected to be. There were never many visitors. A moment later, I heard a car pull up outside and I set the door ajar. Berger came first and on his heels a high-ranking officer in a long great coat with his cap pulled right down over his eyes. He carefully closed the door behind him.

"Himmler," said Berger, with a quick nervous glance at the door, "and his entire staff left this afternoon. It's a fact." He gestured with his shoulder at the great-coated officer, who remained completely passive. "They say more of those with big names will be going to the same place. But that's only a rumor."

"Where?" I asked.

"Got the poster?" parried Berger.

I handed him the newspaper. "Inside," I said. He opened it quickly and folded it up again, and gave the officer a nod. The latter took a matchbox out of his pocket and handed it to me. Before I hurried out, I made certain that there was a word written on it in pencil.

As I strolled through the little park, I opened my hand to see what was on the matchbox. There was only one word, but it was all I needed: Wustrow.

I hurried home and wrote a quick report to the effect that Himmler and his staff were to be found in the small, north German town of Wustrow. I managed to get hold of a courier that same evening. Next day London had the report. SHAEF knew where Himmler and his S.S. staff had gone.

# chapter seven

Would the Russians be able to read? Would they remember? Were they out for revenge? Those were the questions that started creeping through the great city. The Russians were no longer the grotesque devils or slobbering gorillas of the Goebbels's radio, but most tangible foes in flesh and blood, who had come to within a hundred kilometers of the German capital. "Berlin will remain German. Vienna will be German again. And Europe will never be Russian," shouted the propaganda posters, and the Berlin man in the street walked past wondering how to save his little three-room apartment in Steglitz.

The Russians broke through on the Oder front and the Western Powers came charging in from the west. The radio announcement: "No hostile aircraft over the Reich" was changed by those Berlin folk who could still make a jest to "No hostile aircraft over the city." I began to convince myself that my own personal accounting to the German State had been lost in the far greater concerns of the day. The German police had considerably more to worry about than letters of recommendation and border crossings. Accordingly I remained in the apartment. Lili too had moved in.

One morning I was discussing with Carl whether we should dismantle our depots or just take the most vital necessities, in preparation for going underground—in other words down in the cellar—when the siege of the city started. We were interrupted by the telephone's ringing. Carl answered. "It's for you," he said.

It was Ruth.

"Do you remember our little movie talk the other night?" I heard her saying. Her voice sounded unnatural on the phone, monotonous and flat. "I can tell you that they've started shooting it. Would you like to see the first scene? It's a bit uncertain whether or not they will finish any more."

Her usual low and slightly cynical laughter seemed artificial. She might just as well have been crying.

"I'll be right over," I said. "Are you at the apartment?"

"Meet me at the subway entrance on Hohenzollernplatz. But hurry. And if I were you, I'd take a suitcase with whatever you need."

"Does that mean——?"

But she had already hung up.

In great haste I packed a suitcase with toilet things and strapped on my gun holster for the first time. Until now I had regarded it as something slightly ludicrous.

"Does it show?" I asked Carl.

"It looks as if you're toting a billfold considerably fuller than most." He looked gravely from my suitcase to the bulging left side of my coat, but as always in that kind of situation he tried to laugh it off. "Is she so dangerous that you have to dress up like a G-man?"

"I'll give you a ring from town," I said. "Be ready to get

out of here at a moment's notice. No, on second thought, you'd better clear out as soon as I've gone, and take Lili with you. Dump her some place and scout round the neighborhood to see what happens. Let's meet in front of Gedachtnis church, say, four o'clock."

"Something serious happened?" he asked.

"I don't know yet. But get everything out of here."

I found Ruth at the subway entrance when I got there—a slim graceful young girl standing in the sunlight. With one of her unpredictable whims she had dressed up in clothes that seemed like a challenge to the gray uniformity of the square—a white, pleated summer dress and a broad Turkish belt richly embroidered with silver. She wore shoes of alligator hide and carried a light coat over her arm.

Her features were set. She walked across the square a short way in front of me. I didn't mind giving her a lead of three paces because she was attracting a lot of attention. She walked bending slightly forward, tensed, as if she were pressing against some invisible obstacle.

She stopped in front of a dignified, gray apartment house on the square. Before we entered, she looked quickly around in all directions.

"They've gone," she said in a dry voice as we walked up the stairs.

"Who?" I asked.

"My three bosses. I packed their bags. It's barely two hours since they left."

There was no name on the apartment door. Ruth opened it with her key and slammed it shut behind us. In the hall there was a sour, stuffy after-the-party smell. The place looked as if the guests were still there, but had gone to bed. Suspended from the rack and neatly arranged on coat hangers I saw one uniform after another, brown gala uniforms with white lapels, decked with medal ribbons and orders. On the most impressive of all these sartorial masterpieces I spied something that shone brighter than everything else. It was Dr. Ley's gold Nazi emblem.

Ruth opened the door to the living room, which looked as if it had just been left by burglars. Trunks, crates and boxes jumbled together. Clothes carelessly thrown over the chairs. On the sofa still more uniforms, greatcoats and service caps.

"At the last moment they decided to travel as light as possible," Ruth explained in the same toneless voice I had heard on the telephone. "They didn't think there was any need to attract undue attention."

She stood in the doorway and indicated the adjoining study.

I stood for a moment spellbound.

This was indeed chaos! The drawers in the heavy black-stained desk, which dominated the room, were pulled open and documents spilled out across the top. Between the stacks of paper two small valleys had formed, in which there were several upset glasses. On the white background I could trace brown lines, like dried-up river beds, along which the fluid from the glasses had trickled towards the edge of the desk and dripped on the floor. I tiptoed across the carpet that was generously sprinkled with burned-out matches and looked into the fireplace which held a pile of wet, sticky-looking ashes. On top of the ashes there were fragments of glass.

"They started yesterday evening," said Ruth tonelessly from the doorway, "when they heard the Russians had broken through at Kustrin. They kept at it all night. Ley called me up around midnight and told me to come over here. When I arrived they were sorting out documents, but then he decided there was no time for that—we had better burn the most important of them. I tended the fireplace and they fed the piles to the flames. They were already half drunk. I couldn't burn the papers fast enough for them, because they started some crazy gag, seeing who could get there first with a new stack. . . ."

I wandered round the room. I could see that there had once

been pictures in the heavy frames on the walls. They had been removed and in their place there were photographs fastened with thumb tacks, as if tourists had tried to make their hotel room a bit more cozy during a long stay in some foreign town. Some of the photographs were faded grayish brown, others were shiny and new. On a small table by the window there were some large books that looked like snapshot albums. They were spotted with candle grease and beside them a wax candle had burned right down inside the candlestick. One chair looked as if it had been pushed back in great haste from the little table.

Ruth's voice came back again.

". . . . At last they got fed up with burning papers, too. Dr. Ley unlocked a drawer and emptied it, carried a last stack of papers over to the fire and threw it on the flames. He stood there watching the pages curl up and get black, and he said something about iron being tempered in fire before it became steel, that the flames we were watching would purify Nazism and turn it into a spear that would repel all barbarians. All three of them were swaying on their feet but they tried to straighten up, and flung their glasses into the fireplace on top of the ashes in a final toast. The two of them flopped down in their chairs by the desk over there, while Dr. Ley sat down at the small table, and then they went on drinking. All of a sudden Dr. Ley seemed to have nothing more to say, but the two sitting at the desk started boasting about the impenetrable defenses in the south, from which they would commence the recapture of Germany—and only a moment before they had been tempering the spear that would beat back all enemies. Then the lights suddenly went out. . . ." I could tell by her voice that there was something she had to get over by herself.

I looked at the photographs on the walls. Nearly all of them were women, but mostly pictures of Dr. Ley's young wife—I couldn't remember what number. A rather pretty, regular-featured face, a slightly old-fashioned hair style. But then it had been several years before that she committed suicide. She stared down with a calm and, I thought, knowing smile at the chaos around her.

". . . . The drunks at the desk stumbled around in the darkness asking each other with a snigger whether they were already dead, for if so it was a hell of an easy way of dying, and they made loud protests when I brought in the candle and lighted it. When I set it on the table in front of Dr. Ley, I saw that he was crying, whether it was real tears or due to liquor I can't say—but he did cry. He had a big book in front of him and I realized that he had been looking through one of his old snapshot albums when the lights went out. He started talking, not to the two drunks, who had flopped over the desk again with glasses in their hands, nor to me; I suppose not even to himself —just talking into the air, dates, places, names, while his unsteady fingers turned one leaf after another in the album. Eventually his voice grew into a thick, senseless mumble; the glass slipped out of his hand and he fell asleep lying across the album. . . ."

I went over to have a look at it. It told the story of the collapse of Nazism, the result of the misguided ambitions of one man. The album contained pictures from the early days of struggle, the young Ley, in brown shirt and cap, hungry, emaciated and grimly determined. There followed, meticulously recorded on page after page, the all-too-familiar story of the skinny man who grows fat: Ley in more and more gorgeous uniforms, swelling, strutting, supercilious and arrogant, ending with the inevitable apotheosis: Ley on the rostrum, glaring out over a sea of heads in some interminable factory hall. Beneath this large photograph, which occupied a whole page, was written the date July 20, 1944. That was probably when Ley first started crying.

Ruth was still standing in the doorway. I had an idea that she would rather I didn't look at her, as she began to speak again.

". . . . Then when the candle had long since burned down

and morning came, the sunlight fell on Dr. Ley's neck and woke him up. He jumped to his feet and the first thing he said was, 'Has anything happened? I mean. . . .' I just shook my head. He woke the others and they burned documents again until they agreed once more there was no time for that. I would have to destroy them all later. They couldn't stand the sunlight and asked me to pull down the blinds. Then they started drinking again. They told each other how tragic it was that brute force and superior numbers should vanquish higher ideals. But they agreed, on the other hand, that individuals didn't count—people were only the instruments for carrying the idea which would never die but live on and bring about the rebirth of Germany when they themselves were gone. They got drunker and began wondering how near the end might be. They emptied more bottles in a fit of self-compassion, cheering up only at the thought of the wonderful epitaphs they would have, when it became known that they had voluntarily followed Germany into the grave. At last they got so drunk they couldn't pack their things and had to leave it all to me. Two hours ago the car came for them. The driver had to help them down the stairs, as if each had been badly wounded."

The monotonous commentary ceased. For a moment all was quiet. Then I heard Ruth walking through the living room. I threw a parting look at this last Nazi stronghold, where three big shots had fallen and been carried away. A memorial hall that should have been roped off and left as it was. As far as I could see, the documents that had survived were solely of a private nature. I left them for the psychiatrist, who was to be confronted with them later.

I turned around to leave but came face to face with Ruth in the doorway. She was carrying two glasses. Her face was terribly pale. She took a couple of steps into the study, seized one of the half-empty bottles and poured us both a drink.

She raised her glass: "As they claimed—individuals don't count. . . ."

She tossed her head and hurled her empty glass in with the three others on the ashes. I raised my glass to my lips. I had to concentrate on something else and found it: No matter in what circumstances it appeared this was still extra fine genuine French cognac.

"Where did they go?" I asked, quietly putting the glass down.

"To the citadel at Allgau. From there I presume to Switzerland," she answered mechanically, staring absent-mindedly into the fireplace.

"And the others?" I asked gently.

"Gone to earth in the Reich chancellery," she said wearily.

I led her out into the hall. She seemed to get a grip on herself and headed for the door. As I passed Dr. Ley's uniform I stopped and pulled the gold emblem from it, pushing it into my pocket.

Ruth waited at the half-open door.

"You can't imagine the relief I feel now that they're gone," I said, giving her arm a confidential squeeze. "I feel like a free man now. But I don't see why you told me to bring a suitcase."

"The last thing the district leader did yesterday afternoon before coming here was to hand over all the material on your case to his Gestapo friends for their attention."

She slammed the door after us and started walking down the stairs. I stood rooted to the spot.

"We've had a reply from Denmark. Nobody has issued a letter of recommendation to any Herr Schmidt, and no one of that name has crossed the Danish-German border during February of this year."

I walked slowly down to her.

"You can stay at my place," she said. "That's why I told you to bring your things." Then in an effort to regain her usual breezy, slightly disillusioned tone, she added, "After all, what does it matter who sleeps with whom?"

"That, I'm afraid is quite impossible. Besides it would be too dangerous."

She continued down the stairs. When she had reached the landing she turned her head and looked at me with eyes that were completely empty. "I understand. You owe me nothing."

"Oh, yes, I do! And I will do whatever is possible for you as soon as the opportunity comes."

She was hurrying down the stairs. I was not sure that she had heard me, but I was certain that I could read utter defeat in her dejected manner.

From some distance I caught sight of Carl standing in front of the Gedachtnis church. The huge, gutted pile of stone covered with a kind of sooty patina loomed at the end of Kurfurstendamm like a premature monument to the defeat of Germany. I walked up to him and we continued past the bombed movie palace towards Bahnhof Zoo, which from the direction we saw it looked like a giant ocean liner in the process of being broken up.

"They've been to the apartment," Carl said, looking nervously around for the first time since we had been together. "Half an hour ago. In a nice neutral-looking car. Three gentlemen in black. Two of them stayed up there."

"Did you get the apartment cleared out?"

"Yes, to the last cigarette. Pity that one has to be so inhospitable. The radios and the medicine chest are at Lili's."

"And you?"

He looked at me with mild reproach. "What do you think? Same place of course."

We walked along for a while, then I asked reflectively, "Do you think they will trace the car? I'd like to pick up part of the Bernau depot before things start humming."

Carl scratched his nose. "The car? Its origin is long since obliterated in the maze of the black market. And apart from that nobody has as yet given us the sack as diplomats. The C.D. plates are still with the medicine chest. As a matter of fact I thought of Bernau myself."

"Pick me up at noon tomorrow in the car, same place. I'm going to contact Erikson and take him up on his offer to supply me a bed. I think it will be safer that way."

Erikson lived in one of the dignified mansion houses on the Ost-West Achse, the wide impressive avenue that led from the west onto Brandenburger Tor, not too far to walk.

He was sitting in the kitchen peeling potatoes.

"My housekeeper was sensible enough to disappear a week ago," he said with a smile. The kitchen floor was covered with firewood, sacks, crates and buckets of water. In a corner under the window there were piles of rubble and plaster and in the center of this comparatively tidy mess there was an old, rusty stove with a long black iron pipe.

"I'm determined not to eat my potatoes raw," he said with satisfaction, pointing first at the stove and then at a hole in the wall just above the plaster and rubble, through which he intended to stick his own private little chimney.

I had not realized until I stood in this kitchen that the siege of Berlin was more than an expression on the radio, a technical military term. That it was, in fact, a personal problem for every one of the four million inhabitants of Berlin, a pressing question of where to find water and fuel, potatoes and milk, a problem of what to do with babies and dogs, the old and ailing. A giant city that had to be hidden underground. A fantastic thought.

Erikson went on peeling, rinsed the potatoes in a bucket and transferred them to a saucepan. It was wonderful for a change to find someone you could be quiet with. I picked up a knife and started to help him.

When we had finished, I said, "I don't know if you remember that you promised——"

He cut me short. "Make yourself at home. Here or elsewhere in the building. There's plenty of room. You're welcome in the cellar too, but I'm not going down until it gets too hot up here. I feel it my duty to keep an eye on things since I've been given a ringside seat at a historic premiere—or finale if you will."

He started tinkering with the stove. "Dinner at eight o'clock, if you'd like to eat here and if I can get this stubborn, black devil going."

I went into the living room, sat down at a table and wrote the following report to O.S.S.:

> Ley and staff fled to Allgau. Possibly on to Switzerland. Others expected to use the same route. Hitler still in Reich chancellery. Shall I leave Berlin and follow up south?

I put the report in my pocket and went into town to contact a courier.

"It must be about the end of our scuttle-service," he said after taking my message. "Is there much more to report? The events must be speaking for themselves."

Suddenly we both listened. The day had been packed with air-raid warnings. But this was a new one.

"Tank warning," said the courier. "That may be Russian guests for the Führer's birthday party tomorrow!"

"You've all done a wonderful job," I said gratefully. "Send my regards to the other chaps." We shook hands. "You'll see that this gets off tonight? It's very urgent."

He nodded.

"I expect the reply tomorrow. That's important, too. Can you make it?"

He thought for a moment. "We'll have to, but after that I guess the post office will be closed."

I stopped on the stairway in the big house on the Ost-West Achse and opened the message which the courier had been holding for me to collect. It was from O.S.S. to tell me that my two helpers had not made Hamburg, but had been forced to stay in Kiel. From there they had managed to contact London.

Once more I felt the pangs of frustration, as I labored up the many steps to the top floor. Events had developed too rapidly to let me complete my organization and accomplish our final objectives. Little did I realize at this time how useful some of the information in my reports was proving to be. And I might have held my head higher if I had known at the time that my two helpers in Kiel kept London informed to the very last about important German shipping movements in and out of the Kiel harbor, a job which earned them high British decoration after the victory.

"Have you ever seen a Russian?" asked Erikson, when I returned.

"Yes, lots," I answered. "During my childhood in Riga."

Carl picked me up outside the Gedachtnis church at noon the following day, and we drove north towards Bernau on an "inspection" trip. He pulled a small scrap of paper from his pocket.

"Newspapers get easier and easier to run through these days," he said, "but the stuff they print is still the same old story." He pointed at the thick black headline—"The truth, but with the usual little twist."

I took the paper. It was a pamphlet of quarto size, apparently a kind of substitute for the real newspapers that had ceased publication the previous day. The news sheet was titled *Der Panzerbar*—the front soldiers' paper. Under the headline Carl had pointed out, the government informed the inhabitants of Berlin that there was no need to be alarmed if they should hear gunfire around the city in the course of the day. It was only practice firing.

Carl smiled contemptuously and crumpled the news sheet.

128

"They're still pretty good at it. Practice firing—yes, by the Russians!"

Just before reachi g Bernau we landed right in the middle of the "firing practice." Thick clouds of smoke floated above the town, partly from the houses which the Russian shells had set on fire, and partly from the military clothing stores which the Germans had fired themselves. When we got to the old city wall we saw that German soldiers had taken cover behind it, camouflaged with spring branches which they had stuck in their straps and helmets, but their corporal quickly informed us that this was no spring festival.

"On the sidewalk close to the wall if you have to go on!" he said, throwing an angry look at our C.D. plate. "But even in here you move at your own risk!"

We drove on cautiously. I thought, as I had that afternoon on the road from Hamburg, that I would never quite learn to appreciate Allied fire while I was still part of the target. Through one of the city-wall gates we came to an open square which with its dignified, old buildings had a quiet, peaceful and almost neutral air.

Then—so quickly that we hardly had time to wince— there was a whining in the air, a series of explosions one right after the other, and suddenly a dead straight line of craters, spouting earth, stone and splinters, opened up across the square. There was a violent thud in the back of the car as if someone had given it a heavy chopping blow with an axe.

For a moment I just sat there completely dazed and stupidly waiting for the square to relapse into its friendly calm of a few seconds before. Then something came to life in one of the shell holes. A young man—he couldn't have been much more than sixteen—rose from the crater and started to perform a series of ludicrous circulating steps, like a chicken hypnotized by a white circle. During this absurd pirouette he kept his hands clutched at his stomach as if he were carrying some burden he was afraid to drop. Suddenly he flopped over backwards into the crater once more, his hands clutching at the air for support. In a brief glimpse we saw that the burden he had been carrying so gingerly was his own intestines.

I felt the muscles in my face stiffening and I looked over at Carl. He nodded. I turned the car quickly. It seemed to be still running quite normally.

"Is there any other way?" I asked the corporal, when we got back behind the wall.

He waved us on impatiently. "Only the one that leads to Russian captivity," he shouted. "This is no place for civilians. The whole town is under Russian artillery fire. Now get out of the way quick. And mind you don't lose your rear end," he called after us. "You've had a dirty hunk of shrapnel through it!"

Shortly afterwards we pulled up and inspected the damage. The piece of shell must have lodged somewhere in the upholstery of the back seat.

"Well, at least we have a souvenir to take home with us," Carl said, "though I'll bet that kind of thing won't be worth much as a souvenir in a couple of days."

The tank trap before Bernau, which had been open when we drove out, was being closed just as we came back. I stepped on the accelerator and we just managed to slip through the narrow passage in the center of the barricade before the crew in charge of it—elderly home-guard soldiers in uniforms like skiing outfits—swung the last girders in place and barred the road.

"Now it's a race to make the last ferry," Carl said.

I increased our speed. At the next barricade the ski-suited veterans, aided by boys in shorts and black blouses, were pushing an old freight car along a short stretch of track to fill out the hole in the center of the barricade. The fortifications were being closed round Berlin—absurd, almost touching in their improvised insufficiency—frail timber palisades a few yards high, reinforced by a bit of concrete or a few sandbags and manned by old men and children.

"It's going to take the Russians five minutes to get them out of the way," mused Carl as we slipped through the last one. "One minute to blow them to bits and four minutes to stop laughing at them."

I slowed down once more. There were a few things we had to clear up.

"I'll lie low over at Erikson's for a couple of days," I said. "Later I presume the Gestapo will be fully occupied looking after themselves. But there's also a possibility that I'll have to clear right out of the city. It all depends on the message I'm expecting from my chief. I hope the courier will bring it tonight. That'll be the last contact we'll have with headquarters before we meet them in the flesh on Kurfurstendamm. We'll have to abandon the depots until after the capitulation. They will be safest where they are now. If I stay in the city I'll look you up in a couple of days."

"Where?" asked Carl. "I don't care much for going back to the apartment. If they search the cellar, I'll be cornered like a rat."

"I've found a place that seems made for us. You know the ruined carton factory just opposite the post office? Underneath it there is a big, long cellar. I made a little reconnaissance down there during an air raid a week ago. As well as I could do it in the darkness. It isn't exactly a spot you'd choose for a vacation, but it has its advantages. I discovered that the cellar runs into a smaller, separate cellar that was empty. When I asked a man who was down there at the time whether the smaller cellar was much used, he said that no one dared stay in it. It was dangerous, because it was situated immediately below the porch entrance to the factory—nothing overhead to afford protection. Afterwards I went up and looked at the place from the outside. An emergency exit from the small cellar leads directly into the street, and it's protected by two tall piles of rubble from the collapsed factory."

"That sounds perfect," said Carl. "Privacy and our own entrance and exit. What shall I take in case you can come?"

"A transmitter and receiver, spare batteries, the medicine chest—we may need it—and necessary rations. And Lili, if you happen to remember her!"

"That's a date, then," said Carl as I pulled up in front of Gedachtnis church. "No need for the touching farewell, is there? Either you show up in the cellar under the carton factory in a few days, or I'll wave to you when you come marching down Kurfurstendamm at the head of the American army in a week or so. My regards to Erikson."

The transport facilities of the city were just about giving up the ghost, so I had to walk to my appointment with the courier. Berlin still seemed like a living organism that afternoon, admittedly gripped by the pangs of fever, but still breathing. Traffic on the sidewalks was hectic. Food shops had brought out all their stock and people had lined up in long queues in front to collect their rations. Those who had been served started dragging suitcases and sacks, chairs and bedclothes out of the houses. That night the entire city started settling in below ground.

The courier handed me the last message I was to receive from O.S.S. It said:

> Make necessary arrangements for yourself. Suggest you move west before it is too late.

I tore the paper up in tiny fragments and got rid of them on the way back along Kurfurstendamm. I cursed. What kind of message was that? All I could make of it was that there was no enthusiasm for my suggestion of tracking the Nazi bosses on their southward flight.

But why make for the west? My previous instructions had been based on the assumption that the Americans would move into Berlin simultaneously with the Russians, and that I was to contact my department then. I had received no information to the effect that this plan of campaign had been altered.

I stopped for a moment reflectively on the sidewalk, but immediately got a violent shove in the back from a man who was dragging a camp bed. He helped me make my decision. Berlin was the focus of current events, and in Berlin was Carl, for whom I felt responsible until my task was over. There were the depots, which I wanted to hand over intact. And finally—I didn't feel the slightest inclination to leave before the play was over, because I had to agree with Erikson that the closing scenes promised to be a spectacle of no small interest.

He was standing at the window in the living room when I got back. I stood beside him and peered out. The sky above East Berlin was slowly being dyed red. Was it the fading afterglow of sunset or the bright radiance of dawn? I couldn't make up my mind.

Next morning, during Erikson's absence, I wandered around the apartment with a queer feeling of emptiness, unable to concentrate. My host returned shortly after noon.

"Now I'm unemployed," he said. "I was the only one who turned up at the factory this morning."

Suddenly he thought of something and started laughing.

"Oh, yes, there was one more! He was waiting at the gate when I arrived. He wore a smart cap and had a brief case under his arm. Do you know what he wanted? You won't believe it! To check the percentage of waste in my factory! And he was busy, if you please; he was going to other places from there. While the Russian shells are exploding round the streets!"

"Have they started?" I asked eagerly.

"Yes, yes." He went on unperturbed. "I told that fellow in the gold-braided cap, 'Have a good look around and make a note of this: The casks here contain twenty thousand litres of pure spirits of which the waste percentage is 0.32. In eight days there will be zero litres of spirit, and a waste percentage of one hundred. Now you go to your office and reflect awhile on these figures and then come back, if you can spare the time, and tell me what director is going to get the fine.'"

"Where did the shells fall?" I asked.

"Round East Berlin," he answered, but added reassuringly, "Don't worry, our time will come, too."

It did. Later in the afternoon the Russian shells started showering down on Charlottenburg, our district.

A bomb whistles, a bullet hisses, but a shell screams—a ghastly hysterical shrill falsetto. We stood at the window trying to see where they dropped.

"Just as I thought," said Erikson. "The Germans will try to hold the Achse as a line of retreat. I predict a terrific artillery duel, with the Germans defending the Achse from their positions by the Zoo shelters, and the Russians attacking from Spandau. Our street is going to be a perfect firing range and we've got the very best seats—in the middle and high up."

"Shall we go on a quick reconnaissance?" I said, out of sheer habit. I had forgotten that my last report to O.S.S. had been sent off.

"I think it will be better if we remain in our seats," he said, and started putting firewood on the stove. "It's not only the shells making the streets unsafe. The last man hunt for deserters and other sensible people has begun. The rumors exaggerate grossly when they say that they're dangling from lampposts all over the city, but our foreman at the factory told me he had seen one strung up, a poor wretch who hadn't been smart enough. On his chest there was a sign, saying, 'I'm a coward and a traitor. I have betrayed my country, my wife and my daughter,' or words to that effect. People dared not look at him. I suppose, because they were afraid of recognizing themselves. . . . It's a damned nuisance that the papers don't come any more," he added, as he struck another match and held it under the firewood in the stove.

"What I did see was one of the police patrols that are combing the streets and cellars for all male Germans who can still stand on their feet. The worst S.S. gangsters from all over Germany, who have gathered here for one last giant spree. Creatures who are used to shooting first and laughing afterwards. No, I guess you'd better settle down here," he added, blowing impatiently into the stove.

But it was impossible to settle down. I kept wondering whether Carl had got fixed up in the cellar under the carton factory, and whether I should try to get over there. The information about the police patrols was not exactly encouraging. And apart from that Erikson's house was proving a very lively one.

The first shell struck the apartment next morning, as we were sitting in the kitchen occupied with our favorite pastime, potato-peeling, which, according to Erikson was an unjustly underrated occupation. In his opinion potato-peeling brought out the very best in men, promoting meditation and dispassionate reflection. Our meditations, however, were interrupted by a crash that made the kitchen walls vibrate, followed by a still louder crash that covered the potato water and everything else with a white film of plaster. We jumped to our feet and dashed down the corridor. There was an acrid smell of sulphur farther back in the apartment. The living room looked like a woodshed. The shell had entered through the hall ceiling and ploughed through the wall cupboards in the corridor, before exploding in the radio, of which there was not as much as a screw left.

Erikson stood in the doorway which had suddenly become twice as wide as before, and looked appraisingly round the room.

"Must have been a German," he said, "one of those from the battery at the Zoo shelter. If we get more callers they'll probably come from the same place. This apartment faces that way. If it had been a Russian shell, we might just as well have started camping in the open right away."

Later, during the afternoon, we took a trip down to

the cellar, where the general spirit, as far as we could hear, was considerably more cheerful than we had expected. The reason for this optimism was General Wenck's army, which, according to the better-informed cellar strategists, was on its way to break up the Russian encirclement. A few, who had been on visits to neighboring cellars, had even spoken to people, who in turn had met others who had come from the center of the city and with their own eyes had seen pamphlets which stated that Wenck had already reached the suburbs and called upon the shelterers in the cellars to form guerrilla groups and clear the road for him. No one in this cellar lingered very long over that idea. But we did notice that people had started digging rashly into their small store of food, as if they were already taking the general's arrival for granted.

When we came up from the cellar, Erikson stopped to chat with the janitor's wife.

Suddenly the door to the street was flung open and five or six black S.S. troopers, dirty, sweaty, capless, with their tunics unbuttoned at the throat, came charging into the hall and stopped in front of the janitor's office. Erikson jumped aside like a thin shadow and the janitor's wife gave a startled gasp.

"How do you get in there?" asked the leader and pointed with his machine gun to the wall at the right.

"In w-w-where?" stammered the janitor's wife.

"Where do you think?" snarled the leader. "The food and liquor store of course!"

"It's—it's closed," the janitor's wife informed him, trembling.

The blackshirt stamped his foot. "Hell, we know that! But there's always a back door. Get talking, quick!"

A door on the first floor was opened and a man in a dressing gown came out on the landing and looked down.

"What's going on here?" he asked with the voice of an old man, but still firmly.

"What the devil is that to you? Mind your own business,"

shouted the blackshirt rudely; then, to his comrades behind him, he yelled, "One of you keep an eye on the truck."

I stole a glance through the door that was still standing wide open. Drawn up by the sidewalk there was a truck bearing the S.S. mark.

The man in the dressing gown came slowly down the stairs taking heavy steps but holding his back straight. He had a large grizzled beard, and he reminded me of Hindenburg.

The blackshirt kept a watchful eye on him.

"What do you want here?" the old man asked. "Isn't your place elsewhere?"

The blackshirt shouted again, "Where in hell is that back door?" He walked over towards the office, pushing the janitor's wife to one side.

With a swift movement, which I had not expected from one his age, the old man placed himself between them. At first the blackshirt seemed taken aback, then he raised his machine gun and pressed the muzzle against the old man's chest. He didn't budge an inch.

They stood face to face for a moment, the S.S. uniform and the dressing gown. A piercing glare thrust against eyes that never wavered. Then the old man angrily knocked the machine-gun muzzle away from his chest.

"Has it come to this, that Germans shoot Germans?" he asked, his old voice hardly big enough to hold his indignation.

The blackshirt looked at him with hatred but also with impotence showing in his eyes. He shifted the machine gun undecidedly a couple of times and then suddenly struck the old man a violent blow with the gun butt. He turned on his heels and waved curtly to his comrades. . . . A moment later we heard the truck starting up. The old man gathered the dressing gown around him and started back up the stairs.

"He was an army medical officer during the last war," said Erikson.

Next morning the telephone rang. The thin sound came as a surprise in the midst of all the hollow rumbling outside. I picked up the receiver with the feeling that I was initiating an instrument that had just been invented.

It was Carl's voice against a background of distant explosions and blasts.

"Can you hear me?" he roared, so loudly that I had to hold the receiver away from my ear. I gathered that things were pretty hot where he was.

"Yes, if you'll lower your voice a bit," I said. "Where are you?"

"In an empty apartment near the place we spoke about. I just tried the telephone, and it worked. Amazing! That's a hell of a row over at your place. How's it going?"

"Great," I said. "And with you?"

"Over here there's peace and quiet, comparatively, as you can hear. We have settled in where you suggested. We've got it all to ourselves, Lili and I. We were just saying that now we haven't got our own apartment any more——"

I interrupted him. "Don't worry! In a few days even the Gestapo patrols will have moved underground. Then I'll come and see you."

"Are you crazy?" he protested. "This is no weather for taking walks."

I glanced over at the window. Outside a score of invisible express trains were thundering and screaming past at full speed.

"One may be lucky—between showers," I said. "Tell me, did you remember to——"

The line went dead. I shook it agitatedly, but there was no more Carl coming out of it.

"He just quietly faded out," I said despondently to Erikson. "You don't think that——"

"If so, you would have heard the blast," he replied soothingly.

In the afternoon we went down into the cellar again to hear

more rumors. News from the strange underground grapevine that spread its sensations from cellar to cellar and held the great city captive in quivering terror. General Wenck was forgotten, as unimportant and out of date as yesterday. Another army of shadows had marched into the cellars: Horror tales from the fighting in the heart of the city. The screams of the wounded in the overcrowded cellars. Russian fighter-bombers flying at rooftop height above the streets. Raging battles in the pitch-black subway tunnels among thousands of terrified civilians. Flame throwers, tanks, shells and still more shells.

As soon as Erikson opened the door to our apartment the next morning we caught the familiar smell of sulphur. We did not even take time to close the door behind us but went cautiously along the hall. He turned the handle of the dining-room door. It stuck as if there were a strong draught in the apartment. He put all his weight against it and suddenly we tumbled into a room with fine, soft Christmasy snowflakes drifting down from the ceiling. The door slammed behind us, which resulted in the snow now beginning to rise upwards from the chairs and tables. We stood enchanted, if slightly bewildered, and let it settle on us.

Erikson broke the spell. "It's coming through there," he said, pointing to a great, yawning hole in the outer wall. "A bomb must have gone through the cushions and the sofa, moved on through the little room and joined its pal from the other day in the living room, where it has probably turned everything topsy-turvy once more. That's a hell of a snowstorm for a couple of cushions!" he said, holding the shredded covers up in wonder, while he impatiently spat out some bits of down that had gently come to rest on his tongue.

"God knows how my Romer glasses look by now," he said. He dropped the covers and walked over to the sideboard.

"For God's sake look out!" I cried. "There's a hole in the floor, too. Another one must have gone in there. It must have come through the same hole in the outer wall but at a different angle so that it struck the floor. Come over here. I can see it. It hasn't gone off."

Carefully we bent over the hole in the floor and looked down into the apartment below. There it was—a long, slender, black thing, tapering off towards the front and ending in a point. I almost thought I heard it ticking.

"We must get hold of it," I said without enthusiasm.

"Know anything about these monstrosities?" he asked.

"A bit," I answered evasively. I could just about tell its caliber and effective radius. Apart from that I only knew that it was good sense to keep well away from it.

We went down to the apartment below. No one came to the door, but it wasn't locked anyway. We wandered through all the rooms. We met nobody—nor did we find the shell. We looked up at the ceiling in the room we reckoned would be just below our dining room. It was cracked but there was no hole.

"I've been told that the wounds from this war will heal quickly," said Erikson, "but not that quickly. Who has taken the hole? And where is our shell?"

We went back to our own apartment and looked down the hole. The shell was still there. We looked at each other. He felt that his reputation as host was at stake and smiled embarrassedly.

He went out in the kitchen and returned with two large glasses of liqueur. We drank it. And looked. The shell was still there.

Erikson sat down on the remains of the sofa. "I think I've got it," he said, at last. "The room downstairs may belong to the apartment that has its entrance around the corner."

We crept around the corner while screaming shells streaked through the air, hurried up the stairs and tried the door handle. The door was locked.

"Crazy, if there's anyone at home," Erikson said. "If the door shifts slightly in the jambs, they'll be trapped in there."

He rang the bell loud and long. We waited impatiently until we heard shuffling steps inside the apartment.

"Who is there?" asked a thin, quavering voice.

"Open up quickly," we said, rattling the door handle.

"We don't open for anyone. We are old and want to be left in peace," said the piping voice from within.

"All right, you shall be," Erikson called. "Together with the shell lying in front of the rocking chair in your living room!"

There was a gasp behind the door. A fumbling hand started to work on a lot of bolts and chains. At length the door was opened and the face of an old woman with untidy gray hair peeped out. Erikson pushed her roughly aside, and we hurried into the living room. There was the shell, just as we had seen it from upstairs.

"Thank God!" I said.

We stood awhile looking at it. The vicious, slender sting of a giant wasp.

"I wonder what it looks like inside. You said you knew something about——"

I cut him short. "Oh, no, thank you. If I'm to have anything to do with that, it's going to be while it's still in one piece—and that goes for me, too."

Gingerly we each took hold of one end and lifted. When the old woman saw us coming out with the shell between us, she let out a shriek and disappeared into another room with such speed that her thick, gray-white nightgown billowed out behind her like a balloon.

"You're silly to lock yourself in," Erikson called to her, outside the bedroom. Two pairs of terrified eyes peered back at us.

"We just want to be left in peace," wheezed one of the old couple.

When we reached the corner again, we stood looking at each other. The bombardment had increased in fury. It was an absolutely insane situation. Two men with a shell!

"What the hell are we going to do with it?" I said irritably. "Sell it to the Russians?"

We flattened up against the wall. The point of the shell jabbed me painfully behind. A live shell landed on the sidewalk opposite and threw a spray of shrapnel and stone in all directions. We promptly put our shell down and fled back to the apartment.

# chapter eight

During a lull in the artillery duel next morning, I felt that now it couldn't be put off any longer. I crept out into the corridor among all the rubble and took my overcoat down from the rack. It was white with plaster. I started brushing it, a stupid waste of time like shining shoes before going out into the rain. When I turned to put it on, I looked into the disappointed eyes of Erikson.

"I must go and see how Carl is bearing up," I said. "And there are a couple of things I have to arrange. It's high time, if I'm going to have a fair chance of getting through."

I put out my hand.

"All right," he said, "take it easy. Surely I can see my guest to the door. I might add that I'm sorry you're going." He looked despondently around the apartment with its yawning, airy portals. "But of course it's not so cozy up here now; nothing to sit in and less and less to walk on——"

"You know that's not why I'm leaving," I answered as we walked down the stairs. "You've been an exceptional host."

I had reached a tiny park where three streets joined up, when the gunfire started again. First two or three shellbursts like heavy raindrops and then a whole shower sprinkled evenly over the gutted ruins around me. I barely had time to fling myself flat on one of the little lawns with my face pressed down in the grass, so that I could taste the soil between my teeth. There I lay for a while but when the cloudburst of shells grew steadily worse, I raised my head enough to take a quick look around and then crawled on my stomach over to one of the shell craters that had just opened up in the middle of the park. It did not provide much cover, only an illusion of safety, because I tried to convince myself that shells never strike in the same place twice. I stayed in the shell hole for an hour or maybe two, sweating, partly because of my heavy overcoat. By that time I was half deaf from the explosions which incessantly stirred up the rubble piles at the street corners.

At last I couldn't take it any more but bellied my way along the side of the crater until I could look over the rim. I felt terribly lonely. I had to find another human being, hear a voice, see a movement. But the three streets were desolate, a barren lifeless landscape under the savage fury of the bombardment. Desperately I looked around and discovered that I was not alone after all. Under one of the tall trees in the park there was a woman lying on her back, staring with wide open eyes at the new green foliage above her, a small face, set in the slightly stupid, listening expression of the dead. A water mug had rolled away from her when she fell. It glistened under a green lilac bush. Her head was resting against the tree trunk.

I tore my eyes away from the dead woman and let them wander on over to the street corner. They were arrested by a slogan, roughly tarred across the boarded front of some store. The letters were huge and glistened, as if the tar was not yet dry. I just had time to photograph them on my mind before a new shellburst close by sent a spray of stone, earth and splinters up to erase the slogan before my eyes. It read:

# THE HOUR BEFORE DAWN IS DARKEST

It took me most of the day to reach Cicerostrasse, a distance which I normally would have covered in ten minutes by car or bus. But when finally—soaked in perspiration, clothes soiled and crumpled, deaf and stunned, with the stinging taste of smoke in my throat—I stumbled through the porch entrance of the ruined carton factory, I saw to my great relief that my journey had not been in vain. Carl must be there. The heavy cellar door had been provided with a poster in the cool Swedish colors, blue and yellow, which we had hoped would have a soothing effect on any excitable visitors. I didn't bother to read the message written on it in German, English and Russian. I knew it by heart. This place was neutral Swedish territory.

I pushed the door open and walked down some stone steps, feeling my way ahead through the passage in the long cellar without really registering anything but the stench and the darkness, broken here and there on each side by small flickering candles.

I bumped into a German without seeing him and heard his angry curses fade away in the darkness behind me, as I stumbled on, crossed a smaller passage and came to the iron-studded entrance to the little cellar.

"I trust I'm not disturbing you," I said into the darkness and leaned back against the metal doorpost. I heard quick movements, felt hands fumbling for me. One of them took my hand and held it tightly. At the same time a pair of lips kissed me on the cheek.

"Oh my goodness, all that way in all that shelling! I think I'm going to cry."

It was Lili's voice. Everything was all right.

The hand from the darkness loosened its grip on mine. A candle was lit and I looked into the smiling, bearded, dirty face I was so glad to see.

Carl examined me from top to toe by the light of the candle. "You're off your head," he said happily. "What a surprise!"

"The last six hours from Kantstrasse down here were worse than all the days at the Achse put together. There was a stretch of two hundred yards where I was fortunate enough to have the benefit of adjoining cellars. Otherwise I'd never have made it."

"Lili," said Carl considerately, "let's all have a cognac. A big one for him."

"How are things round here?" I asked—superfluously, for I had learned plenty about that on the way.

"S.S. have dug in by the viaduct just over at Hallensee. It cuts off the Russian advance down Kurfurstendamm and consequently the viaduct is under constant fire. Sometimes we get the whole barrage; sometimes we're let off with the ones that overshoot, and that's more than enough. I can tell you the way it goes, hour after hour, all the way round the clock. It starts, increases, grows intolerable, eases up a bit, fades out and then starts all over again. . . ."

There was an undertone to his voice I hadn't heard before, tired, nervous. We raised our glasses that looked like giant, black chalices against the naked, gray walls.

"What's this I'm sitting on?" I asked, passing my hand over something that felt like rough boards.

"Your bed," said Carl. "It's been made up ready for you since we spoke together on the phone, even if none of us thought you'd be so crazy."

"And where do you sleep?" I asked.

"Over there," said Carl, pointing to something long and low by the wall opposite to the door. "I had a hell of a job getting it put together, but the worst part was dragging the boards down here. It's damned difficult to duck with a load like that in your hands."

"Well, what a crazy idea to go tearing around outside collecting boards," I pointed out. "Why didn't you take what you needed right here?"

Carl pointed through the doorway to the dark cave.

"There are more than a hundred in there who wanted beds, too. And they came first. Apart from that I thought it would be more cozy to lie on my own boards instead of on some stranger's."

"What do you mean?" I asked. "I'm not much good at riddles at the moment."

Lili looked swiftly up at Carl. He hesitated a moment and then said, "I tried to tell you on the phone——"

"The house we lived in got it one of the first days," Lili cut in, reaching for Carl's hand. "Our apartment was smashed to bits. Yesterday the last of the façade collapsed. And you know. . . ." She continued after a short pause in which she left a lot of things unsaid. "Carl lived in that apartment for ten years, and it was there we met for the first time. . . ."

I walked over and put an arm around Lili's shoulders. We all sat in silence. Then Carl emptied his glass and jumped up with an impatient gesture, as if he were trying to banish from his thoughts not only yesterday but the last ten years.

"And now I suggest you go to bed and get some rest," he said practically. "Your blankets are at the foot of the bed."

"To bed?" I said looking at my watch with lead-heavy eyes. "It's only five o'clock. What'll I do tonight?"

Carl grinned. "You really are a visitor from another planet. We cave dwellers don't take bedtime so seriously. Sleep as long as you can and don't get up before you're unlucky enough to be wide awake. The surroundings and the music are the same, whether it's day or night."

"But the police patrols," I murmured, my eyes already half closed, "the transmitter, medicine chest, car. . . ."

Blindly I fumbled for the blankets and with a warm if sleepy joy at being home, I felt feeble jaws closing round my wrist and heard a familiar querulous, senile growl. So Uncle Otto was underground too, and even down here ready to defend that, which the old gentleman always, with unfailing instinct, appropriated—my place.

I woke up around three o'clock in the morning. Carl and Lili were asleep. Everything was normal above ground, the thunder coming closer and fading away again. From the bigger cellar I could hear whispering voices and shuffling movements. Small lights flickered briefly in the darkness and disappeared again, but one large light kept circling around in there. I felt wide awake and got up, fumbled for our candle and lit it. The stench, which I had felt like a weight on my chest when I awoke, met me in a concentrated form as I crossed the small passage into the large cellar. A wall in itself of nauseating, stagnant air, human odors, the smoke of firewood and cellar mildew. The light, which I had seen circling without apparent purpose, came moving towards me.

A voice begged, "Give me the key, I must have it," while a trembling hand held a large candle up to my face. I looked into a pair of burning eyes in a face that had become a wilderness of hair and beard.

"The key," repeated the voice, now threateningly. The man waved the candle and I saw the hot melted wax congealing on his wrist.

Out of the darkness came the weary, tortured voice of a woman, "Be quiet now, Pa. There is no key. You know that very well."

Somewhere in the same darkness other voices started cursing irritably. A series of creaking sounds followed—people tossing and turning uncomfortably.

The woman's voice spoke again, just in front of me to one side. "Pa, you're waking the others. Come to bed now."

The man who was looking for a key disappeared suddenly into the darkness at the right. His candle light hovered for a moment in the air as if unsupported, then it too disappeared. I continued along the passage towards the toilet, which I knew lay half a story higher on the landing between the two flights of cellar stairs.

"Pssst!" someone whispered as I had reached the end of the cellar passage. "It's engaged. I'll let you know when it's vacant again." It was an unpleasant lisping voice.

"That's too kind of you. Please don't trouble," I said and turned to go back.

A hand came out of the darkness and grabbed me by the sleeve. "You are new in the cellar?" asked the lisping voice, while the pull at my sleeve grew stronger. Involuntarily I followed and found myself in a small room dimly lit by a tiny candle. The room was no more than five feet square and its only furnishing was a bench behind a wooden box, on which the candle was placed. The man who had pulled me in there straightened the wick and then turned his face towards me, a greasy face with a servile smirk.

"Yes, I live in the cellar under the porch," I said. I couldn't fathom why that should interest this creature. His cheeks moved as if he was running his tongue around inside his mouth to keep his false teeth in place, while he did his best not to relax the servile smirk.

"So, you are one of the foreigners." He nodded with a show of respect. "I took the liberty of stopping you, because I had an idea you were new here. You see, you can always get hold of me if there is something you are not satisfied with in this cellar, for instance if you find someone misusing the toilet, occupying it too long. . . . Or if there are other services I can render. Most people in the cellar look on me as a sort of janitor and come to me with their little problems. I can also get you——"

A woman appeared in the doorway. Instantly he forgot me, jumped up from the bench and bowed. "Was everything satisfactory?" he asked briskly.

I had to admire his choice of words.

"When are you going to clean up in there, janitor? It's insufferable!" the voice exclaimed, in the tea-party falsetto of well-mannered ladies.

"Water is getting short, Fräulein," said the janitor apologetically. "But I will try to do something about it tomorrow."

"And by the way, janitor," the well-bred lady's voice went on, "I need some more candles, preferably of a better quality than the last lot. They were far too expensive. And some cigarettes. . . ."

"At your service," lisped the janitor. His tongue worked energetically round his mouth, as if he were writing the orders in there. The woman's hand held out a small parcel, which he grabbed and stuffed into his pocket.

I couldn't see clearly, but I had an unpleasant feeling that the lady was measuring me through a lorgnette.

"This way, it is vacant now," said the janitor to me. "And don't hesitate to let me know, if there's anything I can do for you."

After three boring hours back on my hard bed, I lit the candle again and went over to shake Carl gently by the shoulder. He turned over, groaned and murmured sleepily, as if he didn't know where he was. "Why do I have to get up? It's still dark!"

I held the candle down to the head of the bed. Lili was lying with her warm young face nestled up against his shoulder. Sleep lent her features a childish, innocent sweetness.

"It sounds as if there's a kind of lull up there," I said. "Let's go up and get some fresh air. I'm just about suffocating."

"Then it's six o'clock," he said with a yawn, raising himself on one elbow. His yawn changed into a happy, almost wondering smile, when he looked down at Lili. Tenderly he covered her with the blankets and got up.

"Say, by the way—tell me how I look," he said, turning towards me. "I haven't been near a mirror for the past week."

"Exceptionally repulsive," I told him. "Gluey hair and a horrible, dirty, bristling beard."

"Okay, then we look alike," he said distastefully. "This damned, everlasting darkness! It dulls the mind. You grow indifferent, stop caring what you look like, unkempt, irritable and insensitive towards others." He nodded towards the large cellar, from which we heard a monotonous sound of moaning. "That fellow starts howling every morning at this time. To begin with I thought it was an awful shame. Now I often wish he'd died during the night. You get that way down here in this hole."

"Come on," I said and went over to the earth steps that led up to a hole in the wall just above the foot of Carl's and Lili's bed. "Give me the bucket and bring the spirit stove and the tin yourself."

The emergency exit was so low we had to crawl on all fours and so narrow we had a lot of trouble handling the water bucket and the spirit stove, especially where the earthen floor rose steeply towards the exit. One side of the passage was made up by the outer wall of the building, the other was plain earth supported with boards. The exit was closed by a heavy, wooden shutter, against which my water bucket clattered. I started tugging at the shutter that abruptly came unstuck.

A wave of golden light rolled into the damp earth tunnel. Blinking, I crawled out through the hole, put the water bucket down and sat on the sidewalk between two high piles of rubble that made a kind of funnel, through which the light and the fresh air streamed down into the little, black hole. I laid my head back, closed my eyes and let the sun beat down on my face. I felt as if I had come from the bottom of a fathomless, black ocean up to the bright, sunlit surface. Beside me Carl started to tinker with the stove.

"Let that wait awhile," I said. "Let's just sit and enjoy it for a moment."

I lowered my eyes to look at the little park across the street. Millions of pearly dewdrops were shimmering in the grass while trees and bushes made up an unbroken haze of green. I thought I heard birdsong too, but maybe that was only inside my own brain, for at the same time I felt strangely deaf and heavy in the head. I drew a deep breath, the familiar stinging mixture of smoke and acrid chemicals, but today there was a faint bouquet with it, just the merest suggestion of the scent of flowers.

"Can it possibly be real—all this?" I murmured, waving my hand towards the greenery. "It isn't something you have arranged?" I wondered idly what the liqueur man would be doing at this moment. I hadn't given him a thought for days. It was amazing how quickly people disappeared out of one's life at times.

"Who, me?" said Carl. "I'm no decorator, only an unappreciated genius in the field of inventing new types of fuel. But there's still a possibility that I may earn due recognition," he added striking a match.

"What is that?" I asked, pointing towards a colorful bundle of rags lying on the sidewalk just opposite the post office. "A rag and bone man who has abandoned his store?"

"That's Heinie," Carl said, matter-of-factly and bent over the stove once more. "I say hello to him every morning when I poke my head out through the hole. He's always there. There's something comforting about him."

"Heinie?" I repeated questioningly. "Does he own all that junk shop?"

"Well, I suppose you could put it that way. He fell on the twenty-first in all his rags, the first casualty in this neighborhood. He's stayed there ever since. I just call him Heinie. He's some kind of slave-laborer."

I looked over at Heinie, lying there on the corner in the sunshine, an anonymous European dressed in a patchwork suit, stitched together from rags and tatters that might have been brought together from every locality between the Balkans and Sakhalin. Heinie, a completely aimless wanderer upon this earth, leaving only one trail behind him—a thin, brown line of coagulated blood which the next shower of rain would wash away. Heinie, whose only epitaph was a few careless remarks exchanged between two cavemen, squatting by a fire in front of a dark hole leading down into the bowels of the earth.

"It's possible that my mixture wasn't much good in an automobile engine, but it's second to none when you want to get the coffee made quickly," said Carl proudly, pointing at the little, white tongues of fire under the kettle. "Each one like a blowtorch!"

I fetched Lili and, sitting on little piles of rubble, we drank our morning coffee.

The last civilized beings in a world that has gone under, I thought, or the first primitives trying to build a new one.

Then the first deep notes of the Russian morning symphony sounded. We gathered up our things, pushed the shutter in place behind us and crawled back down the long, narrow tunnel. The darkness and the stench enveloped us once more.

"It's always worst when you have just been out," said Carl from his part of the darkness. "Then you find it most difficult to get used to the real world—the one down here," he added ironically. He shifted uneasily on his boards.

"That's true. The other one is already like a dream," I said into the dark wall in front of me.

We sat there silently for a while. Then Lili asked, "What's the time?"

I saw a small luminous dial describing a semi-circle in the air.

"The time is seven twenty on a lovely spring morning in late April," said Carl with the same undertone of weariness and nervousness I had heard the day before.

"The trees are dressing for the feast of May and through the small, decorative private gardens wafts a scent of——"

"No, this won't do," I interrupted him. "You've been sitting here for six days—I for only one—but if we don't arrange things in a sensible way, we'll all go crazy. Now let's talk sense. First of all, shall we stop counting on visits from Gestapo and police patrols? Shall we presume that they have plenty to do without looking for us?"

"At any rate we can give them a warm welcome. We have our weapons," Carl answered. "But I guess their time is about up. They won't be coming here."

"Right," I said. "So we'll hide our weapons, say in the emergency exit, so that they aren't here if the Russians turn up, but within reach if the Germans come. Next point! What have we got plenty of?"

"Poison," said Carl, kicking something under his bed, which I presumed was the medicine chest. "And dogs," he added eagerly, as if he had forgotten the most important thing.

"Also canned food, potatoes and liquor, if you don't overdo it," added Lili.

"And what do we have to save on?" I asked.

"Water, candles and the radio batteries," said Lili.

"Right. Then listen to me. We must find something to do, no matter how senseless it may be, make it take as long as possible even to the point of training ourselves to be clumsy so that we'll have to do it all over again when we've finished."

"How about starting on yourselves?" Lili suggested. "Get to look like human beings again?"

"That's it! I was going to start with that, Lili. Carl and I will promise to shave every morning. Lili, you will give us a cup of water and incidentally work out all the other rations, too. Then I suggest we divide the darkness into a so-called day and night and try to adapt ourselves to a timetable.

Lili estimated that we could burn a candle for three hours each day until the first of May. That date had been used so often by history that we felt safe in assuming that something decisive would happen on it again this year.

We set our first candle-hour for twelve o'clock, at which time we shared a can of sausages. After that I took all the neatly arranged little packages, bottles and tins out of the medicine chest and put them just as neatly back again with an unfamiliar and rather pleasant feeling of having done something completely unnecessary. Carl dug a hole in the earth wall of the emergency exit, hiding our weapons in it. Then he carefully wiped the dust off our transmitter and receiver and shook the batteries as if to give them some exercise—also a soothing if utterly useless occupation. Lili counted the potatoes.

Then we blew the candle out. Darkness, dense and impenetrable, returned to our cave, and the dull roar of the surf above thrust itself with renewed strength upon our minds.

I got up and walked into the large cellar. The monotonous moaning voice I had heard that morning was silent now, and there were only a few lights burning, the brightest being two, way down the cellar to the right of the passage. I headed for them and reached the far entrance. The janitor shuffled his feet in the doorway of his little room.

"Shall I get it vacant for you, sir? I see you have no candle with you. I know where——"

I pushed past him irritably and continued up the steps. There were four or five people assembled in front of the toilet, but I didn't mind killing time, even if it was only by waiting.

They were nice, sensible Germans used to queue-culture.

When I got back Carl asked, "Are there many out there?"

"About six or seven," I answered.

"Can we spare a cigarette butt for the janitor? I'm rather in a hurry."

"How ever does that janitor fellow do it?" I asked Lili when Carl had gone. "Black market in the darkness I can understand. But down underground?"

"Well," said Lili, "people who are in a hurry give him a cigarette butt, if they have one, and in return he chases others out of the toilet—others who are not in so much of a hurry but who need a smoke. In that way he gets connections. When somebody needs water or candles or cigarettes, they go to him, and he can always get something, from where I have no idea, nor what people use as payment."

"A ring, for instance," I said, remembering the little package the woman had handed him.

"Maybe. At any rate he seems to be very busy."

"I don't think we ought to patronize him," I said. "His business doesn't make the air any better down here."

Lili agreed with me absolutely.

When Carl returned he said agitatedly, "He's laying across his bed praying again, with two candles lit. And the way he prays! Poor sap, and what a waste of light!"

"Who?" I asked.

"The doctor! The guy at the right of the passage. What a change! You should have seen him the day we came down here, a day later than all the rest. He struck an attitude as if he were the captain of this ship and told us there wasn't room for any more on board—at any rate no foreigners. The others said nothing, but I don't think they minded our coming especially since we came into this little cellar where nobody else dared to stay anyway. We even became quite popular when I put up the little neutral poster outside. I think they look on us as aloof and mystical medicine men, and the poster as a magic taboo that will protect the entire cellar. . . ."

"Aren't you being a bit tough on him?" I said. "When I was on my way over here with the shells hot on my heels, I prayed, too."

"Isn't it getting awfully hot over here by the wall?" asked Lili, shifting uneasily in the darkness.

Neither Carl nor I answered.

"Naturally we all have prayed—the people in there, too— when it started getting too close," Carl finally said reflectively. "That's nothing to be ashamed of. But that doctor guy prays in a nasty, egotistical way, as if he were trying to make some private deal with God—if only He will save the doctor's life, then the doctor will return the favor by giving Him all the rest of us."

"I met another one in the cellar passage last night," I said.

"A queer fellow too, whose nerves were somewhat out of control. He wanted me to give him some key or other. I can't say he made it more cosy in there."

"That's the guy who howls every morning when the Russians take a breather," said Carl. "He's getting insufferable."

"The poor man!" Lili said. "His wife was burned alive when their house went up in flames. The daughter brought him down here. He keeps seeing the burning house, and he thinks his wife is locked in the apartment. That's why he goes around asking for a key. He should have something to calm him down."

"They all should," said Carl. "I could feel the tension in the atmosphere as I walked through just now. They're lying there watching each other. They've slept so much that they're wide awake during the night, too. They've started burning up their candles, because they just can't stand any more darkness. Their nerves are on edge. If one of them starts something, they'll all run amuck. . . . And I won't pretend I don't understand them," he added after a pause.

The seemingly endless, coal-black evening came, broken only by the ten P.M. candle that populated our cave with huge flickering shadows, which made us feel even deeper underground and in the clutches of ghostly powers. Then we undressed in the darkness and neatly laid our clothes on the available boards, but the dampness of the cellar soon routed the temporary improvement of my morale.

We grew more and more depressed until there was even a brief angry exchange of words because Lili, and now Carl also, claimed that the wall on their side felt warm, while I, irritated and shivering with cold, asserted that one always imagined things in the darkness. When Lili asked how one could feel something that was imaginary, I did not even answer. I lay there just feeling ashamed of my part in the quarrel which was the first we had ever had, but I did not have sufficient energy

157

to make the first reconciliatory move. And when Carl threw off some of his blankets, I thought I felt warmer, too, but only from sheer irritation, and shifted uneasily on my boards.

At one time during the night, when I was half dozing, I suddenly bolted upright and groped under the bed where the water bucket was standing. My hand struck something soft which quickly retreated, scuttling across the cellar floor. In my semiconscious condition I could not be quite sure whether it was a rat or a human hand I had just touched. Some hours later I awoke in the same way, but this time I made sure that there was a human hand gently pulling my shoulder.

"I am so sorry to wake you," said the voice of a woman coming from behind the flame of a small candle, "but there is no one out there who can help me. I thought maybe you—as a foreigner—that you might have some tablets or something like that. It's my father. I have watched over him day and night for almost a week now. I can't stand it any more. And I'm afraid of the others."

While I put on a few clothes I heard, coming from the big cellar, the monotonous moan of the man who was looking for a key. His daughter waited for me in the small passage and I followed her down the middle of the large cellar. I had never seen so many candles in there before, and behind every little flame I could make out a white, distorted face—scores of tense, vindictive masks.

"Make him shut up. . . . He's driving us crazy. . . . Throw him out in the yard. . . . For Christ's sake give him that bloody key."

The shouts flew around the woman, who with the tiny bit of candle in her trembling hands stumbled her way through the darkness.

Her father was sitting in a wicker chair, covered with a blanket. Head thrown back, he was howling into the darkness like a dog in the night. The light from the candle fell on his dilated eyes, staring rigidly up at the ceiling, even when I quickly moved the candle to and fro in front of his face. He was the ghastliest corpse I had ever seen—a protesting corpse.

His daughter looked at me anxiously. "I've done all I could," she said, lowering her voice to a whisper so as not to make anyone more angry. "I asked the doctor to give him an injection of morphine. He said he couldn't waste precious drugs on such trifles, but an hour ago the others forced him to do it. It was during the worst of the shelling and the doctor's hands were shaking so much that he broke the needle of the hypodermic. That's why I came to you. . . . I can well understand the others," she added miserably.

"I'll see what I can find," I said.

The noise increased: children cried and people hammered on crates and banged chairs down on the stone floor.

Back in our little cellar Carl had lit the candle. Lili lifted her head in fright from the bed. She was in her nightgown with no covers over her.

"So bedlam has started out there," said Carl. "It's almost worse than the shells."

"The morphine tablets," I said. "Do you know where they are? Hurry!"

"Yes, let's hurry," said Carl. "There are other pressing matters, too."

We got them out.

There were more excited voices now: new ones trying to hush up the cursing and swearing. There were scores of furious private arguments that had lost all connection with the original cause of the disturbance—the old man's penetrating howl. These arguments were nourished solely by the accumulated irritation of seven long, dark days and nights.

We had to put in a lot of work on the old man's jaw, before he swallowed the tablets. We stood by his chair until the howls subsided to a faint whimpering, which died completely as his head flopped heavily over on to the back of the chair. The small, flickering candle flames were extinguished one by one, and the excited voices died away. The cellar relapsed into its normal state of apathy.

"And now another thing," said Carl as soon as we got back to our own cellar. "Will you be so kind as to feel that wall for yourself? If that heat is imagination, I'll go right up and volunteer for the Home Guard!"

I finally consented to touch the wall behind Carl's bed. It was hot as the side of an oven.

"I take it all back," I said. "There's no doubt about it—something's burning. I can't understand it, though. I went up this afternoon to make sure everything was all right, and I didn't see anything. Lili, you'd better get dressed. We're moving into the small passage. This is too risky."

The hands of our watches stood still that night, and the wall grew hotter and hotter, while we moved everything out into the passage. Carl went up to have a look around the yard but had nothing to report, apart from the glow of fires over the city and what we could hear for ourselves—the unceasing shell-bursts. We didn't like to alarm the entire cellar before we had tried to solve the mystery ourselves. A hundred people panicking in the midst of shellfire was not a pleasant thought, but neither was the scorching wall.

At last the six-o'clock morning lull arrived, and Carl and I crawled through the tunnel which felt uncomfortably hot, too.

"Can you see anything?" I asked Carl, when we were lying on the other side of the projecting pile of rubble, looking at the wall.

"No, but I can feel it. It's sizzling hot up here, too."

We lay for a while racking our brains. Absent-mindedly I dug my hand into the gravel pile, letting the pebbles glide through my fingers while I was thinking. It was like grabbing a handful of glowing embers.

"Quick," I said to Carl, "get down in the cellar and shake up the janitor and a couple of strong men. Tell them to bring

160

some shovels and say that if they don't get a move on, the whole cellar might collapse around them."

I found a piece of board and started digging in the gravel. I didn't have to move much before getting to the first glowing coals.

The strong men Carl brought were okay. We shoveled half the coals away during the morning lull and the remainder in the afternoon, digging a wide channel between the wall and the burning coal. When the last shovelful had been removed we all sat down to get our breath, leaning on our shovels.

Carl, wiping his brow, got a black velvet ribbon around his forehead. He asked the janitor, "Who is the owner of that coal?"

The janitor got so busy with his tongue that it looked as if he would stick it right through his cheek.

"Could be a fellow who's really going to work the black market after the war," I suggested.

The janitor flashed me a shifty look. I wasn't sure whether it was an injured or a guilty look for at that moment there was a screaming over our heads followed by another and yet another. Instantly we flung ourselves forward flat on the ground. The shells seemed to be bursting over in the park. A moment later all of us—except the janitor—lifted our heads and over there we saw a vicious, gray-white jet of flame shooting up under a large tree, the foliage of which had been ripped to shreds. We ducked at the sound of a new three-toned scream, and when we looked at the park again, the flame was licking up the tree trunk, but now it seemed more cultivated and dignified—it had taken on a softer hue.

Finally the janitor lifted a brand-new Negro face from the coal dust and looked around in bewilderment. When he saw the flames under the big tree his eyes opened wide like two almost entirely white spheres in his black mask.

"Oh, my goodness!" he cried in panic. "The doctor's car!

There are hundreds of wax candles in it and lots of. . . ."

He jumped up to run over to the park, but one of the Germans grabbed his coat, making him fall.

"Are you crazy?" he cried. "To hell with the doctor's car! It's more important for us to get back to the cellar right away."

As we passed the doctor's quarters on our way back through the long cellar passage, we saw that his constantly burning wax candles had been extinguished. In the light of another German's candle we saw two shadows wildly gesticulating.

"That's the end of the doctor's little private altar and the janitor's profitable business," laughed Carl contentedly. "And if we take the coal into consideration, I think we may agree that it has been a black afternoon indeed for the market."

The luminous hands of our watches turned in the everlasting darkness and told us it was evening candle—and radio hour; then they moved on indicating night-candletime—and bed. But we could no longer sleep and hardly ate. There was an alarming drop, however, in our supply of liquor. In the intense heat from the warm wall the stench had intensified until it seemed almost liquid, and we had a constant taste of lukewarm, putrefied water in our mouths. We lay on our boards talking— stale jokes, platitudes, stupid views that needed no answers— anything to feel the thin thread between us in the darkness. I envied Carl his close contact with another human being and said so. He must have been listening for once, for he laughed, "I'd give you everything—short of that. But I know how you feel."

It was good to hear laughter. A rare experience those days.

Everything repeated itself, monotonous, stupefying, wearing us down. I had never thought of time before because I had always been so busy. Hours, days and years—it had been work and occasional vacation. All the things that had to be seen to, the thousand big or little things of everyday life. Copenhagen, Stockholm and now Berlin. Here we suddenly faced time as an icy, abstract void, as a dimension that knew neither beginning nor end, but seemed to curl back into itself, time as a stationary horror, a black chasm we had no means of filling. And therefore even a dog's death became something of an event.

One night, when I returned from one of my morphine visits to the old man in the wicker chair, I heard contented little grunts, as if one of the dogs had returned in dreams to the bright, green playgrounds of puppyhood. Aunt Elfie, I thought. I had been accepted as a kind of distant relation, and I bent over to fondle the old lady. I was rewarded by an angry yap from Uncle Otto and quickly drew back my hand, after which he went on dreaming. I felt my way across the floor and finally tripped over Aunt Elfie, lying in the corner opposite the one where Uncle Otto was re-living his wild escapades of bygone days. I found this separation of the two ancients so unusual that I woke Carl.

"I think Aunt Elfie is sick," I said. "Uncle Otto has left her."

"Can't you give her half a morphine tablet or something else from the chest?" he said turning over sleepily. "She just needs some fresh air, that's all."

The candle was almost burned down, and I didn't think we could afford to light a new one. In the semidarkness I fumbled inside the chest and broke a little piece off a tablet from the tin. I managed to stuff it down Aunt Elfie's throat after which I carried her over to Uncle Otto. Just as I was falling asleep I wondered drowsily whether it had been the right tin, but then I forgot it again and slept.

At six o'clock the next morning we crawled out into the open once more, Carl with Aunt Elfie under his arm. Uncle Otto came plodding after, close on my heels. He stopped in the middle of the hole leading out to the sunshine, stuck his tail between his legs and turned around to creep back down the black tunnel. I grabbed him by the scruff of the neck and put him outside of the rubble.

163

"Aunt Elfie suddenly went all heavy," Carl said. He lowered her gently to the ground. "What's the matter, Aunt Elfie?" he coaxed worriedly, bending over her.

She rolled as far over on her side as a sausage can. The only thing wrong with Aunt Elfie was that a long and eventful dog's life had come to its natural conclusion.

Carl looked at her in utter bewilderment for a moment, then he swiftly turned his face away.

"Take it easy, Carl," I said. "Practically speaking Aunt Elfie has been dead for a long time. And what's a dog compared to all the other things happening around us?"

He held his hand over his eyes as if shading them from the sun. "I know that, but don't laugh at me. I can't help it. She was always so happy to see me and so miserable when I left. And how many have felt that way—for thirteen years?"

I looked at Uncle who was circling his dead mate and sniffing at her with obvious signs of revulsion.

"You still have Uncle Otto," I said consolingly.

"It will never be quite the same again," said Carl, still averting his face. "Not for Uncle Otto either."

I didn't have the heart to ask him to look at the broken-hearted survivor. For the first time during our acquaintance Uncle Otto was walking on his paws, and he seemed to be occupied with something as frivolous as chasing a fly.

Aunt Elfie was buried by me alone. I dug her grave and carried her to it. Afterwards I placed a couple of bricks as a little cairn over the mound and sat down on it for a moment. Automatically my eyes sought Heinie, still lying there on pavement. With a vague feeling of guilt I reflected that it's purely a matter of chance where one finds a grave in this world.

Another forty-eight hours rolled by like blacked-out trains, roaring, rumbling, thundering, clattering and shaking their way through an endless, dark tunnel. All topics of conversation were exhausted, all jokes told and retold, all the batteries run down, inside ourselves as well as in the radio. The last mouthfuls of water tasted of sewage. Lili marked off our last candle in three equal sections, scratched in the wax with the point of a knife.

"We have three lots of twenty minutes left," she said in a very small voice. "Or would you prefer to squander it all in one go?"

"In one go, of course," said Carl. "Tomorrow we're getting out of here, no matter what's going on outside."

We burned our last candle at two o'clock that morning. We sat on our boards staring into the little flame, burning gently on the wooden crate in the middle of the cellar floor. I don't know what the others felt, but I thought of the first Christmas I could remember, when my small greedy hands had made a grab for the bright objects between the green branches of the tree. I burned my fingers and my mother said a lot of loud words. And I remembered how I missed the little, bright objects afterwards when I lay alone in my bed in the darkness.

Later, when the candle had burned almost all the way down and only a tiny tongue of flame quivered at the end of the charred wick, and lots of other thoughts had rushed through my brain, I finally saw before me an inscription, tarred in enormous black letters, which at the next moment were obliterated in a rain of earth, stone and splinters from a bursting shell.

The light flickered and went out. I raised my head and, with the gleam of light still behind my eyes, I spoke in a low voice over towards the others, "The hour before dawn is darkest."

It was some time before Carl answered; then he murmured wearily, "And the longest."

Lying there on our rough beds, we suddenly heard a lot of noise and disturbance coming from the large cellar. The noise increased and loud voices resounded through the cellar vault.

I grabbed Carl by the arm and we tiptoed across the corridor to peer into the big cellar, which for the first time was comparatively well illuminated. The situation did not permit lingering on details, but I got a general impression—the stinking, chaotic, overcrowded passenger-hold in an emigrant ship of the last century.

The light came from some powerful torches in the hands of a dozen dark figures that were gathered in a close group at the end of the passage. The massive body of men had a defiant attitude, like people pressed close together for the last defense. One of the dark figures detached itself from the group and came forward. His shadow loomed huge and ill-boding on the ceiling.

"Get your clothes off, and be damned quick about it!" he shouted. "We've been lying up at the viaduct four days defending you without food or drink. Now you take over! We've had enough!"

A short, black shadow jutting out from the big one moved jerkily. "You there!" cried the black figure. "And you! And you over there. . . ." He strolled slowly down the passage, pointing his machine gun at the bed spaces. "Hurry, you bastards! If you think we're kidding you're crazy!"

From our cover behind the wall Carl and I watched the strange strip tease. The S.S. men strolled down the passage pulling off their uniforms which they flung over on the beds. On the way back they grabbed the civilian clothes which the terrified Germans held out to them. The nocturnal guests stopped at the end of the passage where a flurry of arms projected giant shadow-pictures across the ceiling. Then the group—now made up of a dozen gentlemen—gathered once more. Not very tastefully dressed but otherwise convincing enough. As civilians, they made their way out of the cellar.

# chapter nine

We squatted down in our little enclosure between the two piles of rubble boiling water for our last shave. Down in the cellar Lili was packing our things. The previous night's decision not to stay in the cave another day remained unchanged.

"Where shall we go?" I asked, sitting despondently down on the little cairn over Aunt Elfie's grave. "Lili can't make the trip over to the liqueur man's apartment—even if there should be something left of it."

"Let's slip over to Lili's place during the afternoon lull," said Carl. "It's a solid house and her room is on the ground floor. It's only four blocks away from here."

He looked at his watch. "That's funny. It's just seven o'clock. They're usually very punctual!"

We sat for a while looking around. There was no reason to go down before the bombing started again. It was good just to sit and gaze at the green of the park, relax our tensed muscles, let our jaws drop open and not give a damn if we did look foolish.

Carl looked at his watch again and I followed suit. Unconsciously we were straining our ears to hear the sound we expected to start at any moment. The indifferent relaxed feeling was superseded by an absurd urgency to feel the pain again rather than sit around waiting for it. Another half hour went by. We listened tensely. It was as if even the remaining trees over in the park were listening, and Heinie too, from his sidewalk corner.

Suddenly Carl jumped to his feet. "It's over!" he shouted.

Frightened by the sudden sound of his own cry, he looked cautiously around on all sides. Then he rushed over to me and grabbed my hand in exultation. "It's over!"

He bent down and shouted through the black tunnel, "It's over! It's over!"

The cry bounced back to him as from an empty room. There was no real response to his enthusiasm.

Shortly afterwards when we had calmed down a bit, problems started confronting us. Historical moments never last long. Hardly has the scene been decked with festive flags and bunting, before a host of little black devils, flouting everyday problems, set out to tear it down again.

"It's going to be strange without you," said Carl, "after all we've been through together."

"I feel as if I had known you always," I answered. "But the job is done now. All that's left for me is to join my section and make a final report. How do you suppose the Russians will transport me back to the American lines? I hope it'll be in one of our own jeeps. I'm interested to see if there can really be so much in so little."

"I would have been happier if the Americans and British had been here, too, instead of down by the Elbe," said Carl pensively. "I won't feel really liberated until they turn up."

"That will probably be some time this week," I said. "I guess this has been arranged for a long time, but they must have forgotten to tell us about it. Now I suggest that you take

Lili over to her place as we planned. I'll go out and get hold of some responsible Russian who can lead me to an intelligence officer. Then I'll try and persuade him to send me back to my own lines as well as to protect you two if your Swedish citizenship shouldn't prove sufficient. We'll leave the weapons where they are. They might easily be misunderstood. But I'd better take care of the transmitter and the medicine chest myself. They'd only compromise you, while I can use them in an emergency as a kind of proof that I really am what I claim to be."

I suddenly realized that they were my only means of identification apart from the counterfeit passport with the German stamps, which I was not too keen on displaying.

For the last time we crawled through the tunnel back to the little cellar. There were about a dozen Germans in there with Lili. The cellar door leading to the courtyard had been opened and a gray, dismal light seeped through to us. Even in this dim light I could see that the German faces, far from showing relief, looked nervous and apprehensive.

"It sounds terrible," said Lili, pressing close to Carl. "They say the Russians are raping women. . . ."

"You must protect us," said a respectable-looking, elderly German clutching urgently at my sleeve. "You must tell them this is neutral embassy ground. It is ghastly. They feel their way through the dark cellars and pull the women from their beds. Old as well as young. Two or three Russians to a woman. We can't do anything. If we move we are shot down. I have my wife and a half-grown daughter in there. I just can't bear to think about it. How can people behave like that? Is that the revenge?"

The other Germans looked at me. I felt uneasy. This was something quite new and horrible, if it were true. I felt it my duty to defend my allies.

"It's probably greatly exaggerated—an isolated incident that has been magnified and has fostered a lot of rumors. In this chaos you're bound to get certain episodes here and there.

Don't forget what war can do to people. Soldiers who have been on the march for maybe as much as five years, lived through everything that's vile and filthy on this earth—how do you expect them to turn out? They get used to taking what they can get, while the chance is there. You spoke of revenge. Don't forget, either, that the Russians have a great deal to avenge."

The elderly German looked at the others and then bent his head, starting to study his shoes.

"We know that—now," he said quietly. "It is as if we all, during the past few months, have found the courage to tell each other what we knew, the things we had not dared to mention before. But turning on the women! That's a dirty revenge!"

I could only respect his attitude.

"Naturally I agree with you there," I said, "but let's hope it is all exaggerated. My friend and I have done all we can do for you at the moment. I'm sure the Russians will respect the Swedish poster out there."

A young girl came rushing in from the other cellar, stopped questingly on the threshold of ours, then ran over to the German who had just spoken, clinging to his arm.

"Oh, it's so terrible, Father," she said agitatedly. "I've just heard what happened to the dark-haired girl from number five. The one we knew was half Jewish all the time, but who managed to get away with it. She went upstairs early this morning from the cellar next door with her yellow Hebrew star pinned to her breast, because she thought that would keep the Russians from doing anything to her. She dragged herself down into our cellar just now. They raped her in the yard, right in the middle of the cobbles. . . ." The girl hid her face in her father's sleeve.

Another of the Germans said, "I'm told they are breaking into the liquor store around the corner. Just imagine when they're good and drunk and start. . . ."

I looked from one German to the other. Would a Swedish

poster make a greater impression on the Russians than the Hebrew star?

"I think time's getting short," Carl whispered to me.

I took off my watch and slipped it into my pocket. "Stay here until I get back," I answered quietly. "I'll try and fix it as quickly as possible."

The passage through the large cellar was blocked by numerous little groups, each group a small German family, mostly mothers, children and old people. They stood pressed closely together their anxious eyes following me. At the end of the passage I glanced into the janitor's little room. It was empty. I took the cellar stairs in a few leaps and hurried across the yard through the porch. The street was absolutely still, and there was no movement over in the park either. Smoke was rising from an apartment house on the other side of the park, and from the center of the city I heard the distant rumble of explosions. I pushed my hands in my pockets and quickened my pace. My fingers were toying with something round and hard, while I was wondering how I could best introduce myself to my allies. Suddenly I whipped my hand out. The thing I had got hold of was at any rate the worst possible introduction. I threw a cautious look in all directions, and then I flung Dr. Ley's gold Nazi emblem far away into some green bushes. A moment later it was followed by Dr. Best's letter of introduction.

I didn't see my first Russians until I had almost reached the corner of Kurfurstendamm. The impression I got was rather an anticlimax. They were two very ordinary young soldiers in black boots and brown uniforms that bore the unmistakable signs of having recently been in the thick of battle. I could hear a great deal of noise coming from Kurfurstendamm, but for the moment I was too occupied with my own Russians to pay any notice. It was almost too touching! The two soldiers were helping an old woman up the stone steps of a large house, like a couple of zealous Boy Scouts. She had probably come directly from the cellar. Behind her walked a young girl carrying a bundle. The last thing I saw before they all disappeared through the door was one Russian politely relieving the young girl of her burden. I hurried over and entered the building after them. What a stroke of luck running into those helpful and obliging fellows. They would probably tell me where to go.

I was suddenly startled by a piercing shriek echoing down the staircase. Another voice started moaning and whimpering and a lot of feet were trampling and kicking on the stairs. I stood for a moment with my hand on the bannisters, overcome with revulsion and helplessness. But it was no use for me to interfere. I had my own mission, and I was in a hurry. I walked outside again with the wild shrieks ringing in my ears. I wondered whether the helpful Russians were raping the old woman too.

Vastly more reserved in my opinion of the liberators of Berlin and increasingly skeptical with regard to the solution of my own problems, I turned down Kurfurstendamm. This was a street I no longer knew: a long junk yard full of rubble, old iron, shattered vehicles, twisted lampposts and entangled cables all lightly veiled by the smoke from the smoldering ruins, the profiles of which I did not recognize either. Along the traffic lane just opposite me heavy Russian armored cars were plowing their way through the junk towards the center of the city. I swerved around the bloated carcass of a horse feeling the stench from it like a spray in my face, waited for a break in the Russian traffic and then quickly crossed the road to the wide green strip of grass along which the trolleys had once moved. I tripped over the remains of the low iron railing and cursed because I got one shoe stuck in it. While I was getting it free I looked over at the other sidewalk, which was jammed with shouting and laughing soldiers in dull, brown uniforms, long rows of them arm in arm. Just off the sidewalk in the road six or seven German cars were being driven round among each other like Dodgems at a fun fair. Drunken shouts and raucous laughter rose from the cars, too. I looked around desperately. Wasn't there one single Russian who might be sober and through with the hunt in the cellars?

A small car which, as far as I could make out, might be a German Red Cross van, came tearing round a corner on two wheels. The driver was about to lose control over it, but in the last moment he managed to get it straightened up and continued a bit more slowly down the road towards the spot where I was standing. I noticed that the Russians in it were wearing peaked caps and must therefore hold some kind of superior rank. I stepped over the twisted railing and put a hand in the air.

"Amerikansky!" I shouted through the open window of the driver's cab as the van shot past me. It pulled up hard, but even so was quite a distance away before it stood still. I hurried up to it.

Three peaked caps looked cautiously through the window, one on top of the other.

"Amerikansky?" repeated one strange and curious foreigner in a crumpled suit. He put out his hand and did his best to smile. "Congratulations," he said.

"Americansky?" said the cap behind the wheel reticently, but without animosity.

We sized each other up like members of two strange, wild tribes who, by chance, have run into each other on the hunting grounds of a third.

"Your commanding officer? Where can I find him?" I asked.

The members of the other tribe started to whisper among themselves. A happy Dodgem driver brushed past close to me. Then one of the caps gestured over his shoulder while the one at the wheel shrugged deprecatingly, as if to say that there was no more room. I turned on my heel and continued in desperation down the road to find a Russian who was not occupied in some way or other.

"Amerikansky!" someone shouted behind me. I saw that it

was the cap behind the wheel. He also pointed over his shoulder with an obliging grin. This time I caught on and scrambled into the rear of the ambulance. There were a great many bottles rolling up and down the floor and they banged against my thighs. I cooled my hands on a couple·of them, as I looked through the open doors. The trolley wires were hanging brokenly down from their masts. At the very top of one mast the wire net had been entangled in something that seemed to be wrapped in an old dress. It was not until I noticed a leg with a black shoe sticking out of the bundle, that I realized it was the remains of a woman hanging up there.

We didn't drive very far, but we moved at a breakneck speed. The driver pulled up in some side street and I jumped down. He pointed to a factory building with large windows facing the street. When I got in there I felt a lot of inquisitive eyes on me, but I made straight for one of the windows where a tall, broad officer in a long greatcoat was standing with his hands clasped behind his back, staring out into the street. My arrival could not possibly have escaped his attention, but he never moved an inch when I said, "Amerikansky! I wish to speak to an intelligence officer."

I shuffled my feet on the floor and repeated my request.

Finally he turned his head and gave me a totally expressionless look through the thick lenses of his spectacles. What I could not read in his eyes, I heard in his voice, which sounded thick and hoarse as voices do after several nights of wakefulness.

"Not here," he said indifferently. It caused him considerable effort to take his hands from his back and point to a spot farther down the street. I followed his indication and memorized the place. Then I looked at him questioningly again.

"The political department," he said in a tone that told me the interview was over—irrevocably over.

The caps had driven off again, and I hurried down the street to the house the officer had showed me. Fortunately there could be no doubt as to where the Russian Political Department for West Berlin had established itself. It was the only open door in the entire building.

The room was cozy with blue curtains and heavy, dark furniture. A Russian was sitting at the table in the center of the room eating something from a tin with an absurd little spoon. His greatcoat and gun holster were slung over the back of a chair beside him.

"American officer," I said. "Have been operating behind the German lines. Request to be transferred to my own people."

The police officer raised his eyes from the tin. He looked at me briefly, whereupon he followed the spoon as far as he could, until it disappeared into his mouth.

"Tomorrow," he said, chewing. He was newly shaved and his round face shone ruddy and bright.

"Tomorrow it will be too late," I shouted desperately, tripping over the words. "I'm an American agent. All my equipment, transmitter and drugs are lying unprotected. I demand as an ally that you give my case fitting attention."

The Russian wiped his mouth and looked deep down into the empty tin.

"In German," he said. He nodded at another man who sat just inside the door on the edge of a chair with his feet close together under the seat. The man jumped up and stood rigidly at attention.

I repeated more calmly—and in German—what I had blurted out in Russian. The Russian slave-laborer started his career as interpreter to the Political Department by translating dutifully.

"We have more important matters on our hands," said the police officer picking up his greatcoat. Underneath it there was a fur cap. "Ask him to come back tomorrow," he added and got up.

The interpreter translated what I had already understood.

"I must get in touch with staff headquarters," I persisted. "I have valuable information."

175

"So far we have managed without the help of others," answered the police officer through the interpreter. "And now you must excuse me. I'm busy."

I had hoped for helpfulness and feared suspicion. Complete indifference was the only thing I hadn't expected. I tried a last—and I feared a vain—appeal to this member of a foreign, mysterious tribe.

"It's just around the corner off Kurfurstendamm. Maybe we could drive to headquarters in my car. I've got it parked there——"

"Your car?" exclaimed the police officer and the interpreter with one voice. The Russian officer had picked up that much German, then! For some reason this changed the entire situation.

Though it was a scorching hot day, the Russian officer put on his fur cap, which surprised me no more than all the rest. "I'll see what I can do for you," he said, addressing me directly in slow and distinct Russian. "We can leave at once."

The interpreter kept at a respectful distance as we walked down the street. The police officer was suddenly in a most excellent mood, which I took advantage of to get him interested in my completed mission in Berlin and the possibilities of being transferred to the American lines right away. He listened politely, the way people do when they're waiting for you to pause for breath so that they can start talking themselves.

"Is it a good car?" he inserted during my inevitable pause which lasted a bit longer than I had intended because on the sidewalk, right in front of me, I suddenly saw a small, black arm sticking out between the stones in a heap of rubble. It looked as if the arm was eagerly showing the way to something, but what it was I couldn't tell, because the arm had no hand.

We walked around the rubble heap. The police officer looked expectantly and a little suspiciously at me, and I hastened to answer.

"The car? It's a Mercedes, in excellent condition." I

pointed across Kurfurstendamm. "It's the side street just over there. It will only take two minutes."

We made our way carefully through the network of fallen cables and slipped across the traffic lane where the Russian armored cars were still rattling towards the center of the city. A fallen German soldier was being run over again and again by heavy Russian wheels—as though he were a small, red rug spread out for the victors.

When we turned down Cicerostrasse, I saw a figure stumbling out from a porch way down the street. It was some time before I realized that it was our porch, and that the figure was Carl. I broke into a run, leaving the police officer and the interpreter behind. Even at a distance I could tell by his reeling movement that something was wrong, and when I came closer I saw blood trickling from one corner of his mouth.

I grabbed him by the shoulder. "What's happened?" I asked breathlessly.

"They've got hold of Lili," he panted. I turned and waved frantically for the two Russians further up the street to hurry. Then I supported Carl as quickly as his unsteady legs would carry him back towards the porch.

"Some Germans—came tearing in from—the big cellar," he said, gasping for breath. "They said there were—half a dozen Russians—outside the cellar door—looking at the poster. The Germans begged me to go and talk to them. I told Lili to stay behind—and hurried into the big cellar. Just as I passed the janitor's room a huge Russian came down the stairs. I wanted to stop him, but he shoved me aside and went straight for someone behind me. I heard a scream and I knew it was Lili—she had followed me after all. I jumped for the Russian—but he struck me in the face and I fell against the wall. I can't remember—how I got out here. . . ."

As we turned into the porch I looked back and saw that the police officer and the interpreter had quickened their pace. There was a group of Russians gathered in front of the poster but I only got a brief glimpse of their gesticulations as I shot past them down the cellar steps. The door of the janitor's little room was shut and the sight filled me with uncontrollable fury. Lili, sweet, lovely Lili and that filthy swine!

I wrenched the door open and in the semi-darkness I saw Lili, her hair and clothes disarranged, being pressed down against the wooden bench, the broad, powerful back of a Russian bending over her. He turned in surprise and for a brief moment he must have lost his balance for I managed to swing a blow in on him so that he staggered. I heard someone else coming through the door. The Russian waved his arms but I caught hold of them and forced him against the wall. "His gun, Carl," I gasped. "Get his gun!"

The Russian twisted to get free. His curses reeked of alcohol. He tried to shove a knee in my groin but didn't quite make it, though it hurt like hell. I retaliated by giving him a vicious kick on the shins. I calmed down a bit when I realized he was half drunk and unable to control his movements, but just to make sure I gave him another resounding kick. It gave me intense pleasure to see his face distorting with pain. Carl led Lili past my back out into the passage, and I thought it was crazy because the others might come any moment, and then I suddenly heard an angry voice booming, "What the devil is going on here?"

I turned my head and saw the police officer's livid face. He stepped into the small room pushing me aside.

"What's the meaning of this filthy behavior?" he shouted into the face of the Russian soldier, who froze in the position in which I had held him, with his arms pressed up against the wall.

"This is Swedish property," I said, "a neutral area. And still one of your men assaults my friend's wife, a Swedish lady. Is that worthy of the Russian army?"

I spoke in a mixture of German and Russian, but the police officer got the meaning of it and stared furiously at the soldier, who was doing up his belt with a sheepish grin. Without warning the police officer whipped his revolver from his hip and with a violent movement chopped the butt into the face of the soldier, who doubled up hiding his head in his hands.

"Swine! Filthy skunk!" roared the police officer giving the soldier a shove that sent him reeling. "Get a move on!" he ordered and dug his gun into the back of the other, who, half blinded by blood, started stumbling down the cellar passage. I followed, wanting to see him as far removed as possible.

The other Russians were still standing in a group by the cellar entrance, rooted to the earth in front of the magic poster that had caused all the disturbance. But when their comrade appeared with the police officer's gun in his back, they came to life and split up into two rows, one on each side of the cellar entrance, grinning and pointing at him.

The officer drove the culprit between the rows and the scene became an improvised running the gauntlet. The soldier, stumbling along with his face covered by his hands, received a well-aimed blow from each of his grinning comrades. When he banged into the wall of the neighboring house, he straightened up, pressing his back against it. The police officer took up position with straddling legs in front of him, roaring and cursing him, while the other Russians gathered around them jeering. The culprit lowered his arms and he looked at the police officer with an expression of mute appeal on his blood-smeared face, while his hand fumbled across his tunic breast until it reached the small cellophane bags, hanging in a neat row and containing all his decorations. The last I saw he had gathered all the cellophane bags in his hand and was holding them out towards the officer. Then, followed by the echo of the officer's curses I hurried back through the passage to the small cellar.

Lili was sitting on the bed. She had fixed up her dress and brushed the hair off her forehead.

Carl was bending over her and I could tell by his attitude that he was quite himself again. "Thank heaven, he didn't get time," he said in a trembling voice. "If he had just had one more minute——"

"Let's not talk about it any more," I interrupted. I remembered that Lili was only nineteen years old.

She looked up at Carl with amazing calm and said, in a voice which she tried to make equally calm, "It has to be told some time. I would rather get it over now. Afterwards I will never, never think of it again."

She paused to get hold of herself. Then she said, "He wasn't brutal or violent—to begin with. He let me sit on the bench and I played for time by pointing at all his decorations. I let him think that I was deeply impressed, and he said a lot of things I didn't understand. When that didn't work any longer, I pointed through the door up to the yard as if to suggest that we should go to some other place. But then he started getting impatient. He drew his gun with one hand and with the other. . . ."

She didn't lower her eyes, but they suddenly grew searching as if she were anxiously seeking Carl's reassurance that she had not lost anything as a woman.

"But you saw that for yourselves," she went on in a weaker voice. "No, I can't tell you after all." She broke down, hiding her face in her hands.

Shortly afterwards the three of us walked into the big cellar, I in my overcoat with the transmitter in one hand and the medicine chest in the other. The police officer was standing in the center of the passage proffering his open cigarette case. The Germans had gathered in a circle around him, but kept well out of his reach, shuffling their feet, wondering whether they dared move closer or whether they should run away.

I walked up to him and pulled his sleeve. He snapped his cigarette case shut, sent the Germans an offended glare and concentrated on me. "Ah, the car!" he suddenly remembered, brightening up considerably.

"There is something I must request of you first," I said.

"My friend and his wife have helped me on my mission here. You must see to their protection."

"Naturally," he said obligingly. "Got a piece of paper?"

I fumbled through my pockets. The last piece of paper I had carried on me had fluttered in tiny fragments into the bushes that morning. Now I only had my counterfeit passport. I turned to Carl. "Have you got a piece of paper?"

He thumbed through his notebook which the police officer looked at with great interest and suddenly snatched out of his hand. Carl had got to that page in the calendar which marked the birthday of the Swedish king and carried a portrait of him.

The Russian glared at the king. "Nicht gut," he declared and turned the page.

Carl and I looked at each other bewildered. Whatever could this Russian have against the venerable Swedish monarch?

The Russian wrote something on a blank page, ripped it out and handed it to the interpreter. "Your friend and his wife will be escorted to their residence and this pass, which your friend can have made more official at my office tomorrow, will prevent his being involved in further misunderstandings. Now, are you ready to go?"

I looked from the scrap of paper to the interpreter, but it was probably all we could get. Carl read my thoughts and said impatiently in Swedish, "Now you must do something about yourself. We'll manage all right. Anyway we'll be seeing each other soon again. Don't think of us any more, but grab your chance and get going. The guy here seems to be a little different from the rest."

I caught Carl's and Lili's hands simultaneously and shook them warmly. Then I hurried after the police officer, who was already moving up the stairs.

As we drove down Kurfurstendamm the Russian pushed his fur cap off his forehead, leaned back in his seat and waved towards the sidewalk, which was now teeming with Russian soldiers.

181

"You see," he told me in a lecturing tone of voice, "misunderstandings like the one we have fortunately just prevented will inevitably take place, as in all armies that have just conquered the capital of the enemy. But we officers have received strict orders to intervene against digressions of any kind. We wish to show the world an example of Russian self-discipline."

We stopped in one of the squares in front of a large, comparatively undamaged block of houses.

"Now I will forward your case," he said. "You stay here. I'll only be half an hour."

He looked out over the square and back to the car. Then he beckoned to a Russian private who was passing by and pointed to the seat he was about to abandon.

"I don't want anyone to touch this car, understand?" he ordered with a threatening look at the private, who, with obvious annoyance, slipped into the seat.

The police officer disappeared into the building and left me to my thoughts. He was right—about the misunderstandings if not about the self-discipline. Russian soldiers, shouting and laughing, swarmed all over the square, dragging armfuls of things they had looted from the houses that were still standing: clothes, crockery, lamps, candlesticks, barometers, vases, pictures and bottles. Some of them suddenly dropped whatever they were carrying and rushed into a new house, from which they had seen comrades emerge with more enticing burdens. The sidewalks round the square were littered with both junk and valuables, everything helter-skelter, trodden on, kicked aside, picked up and flung down again. That day the Russians turned what still remained of Berlin literally inside out. The wrecked city became one enormous junk shop, where the door was wide open and where thieves were the policemen, too. And in the meantime the hunt for women was still on.

At the stairs leading up to the S-bahn a Russian had grabbed hold of a woman in a black cloak. She screamed and struggled while the Russian tried to overpower her. He had set down his bundle on the step below and during the struggle her foot struck the bundle, kicking it down on the sidewalk. Another Russian came strolling past. Without so much as a look at the tangled confusion of brown and black on the stairs, he bent down and untied his comrade's bundle. He went quickly through it, tied it up again and hung it on the barrel of his machine gun, leaving his own bundle in its place.

I turned my eyes away from the stairs and tried to close my ears against the screams of the woman. Naturally I felt an instinctive, human desire to go to her aid, but I knew it was hopeless. Everywhere in the streets of Berlin, on staircases, in the parks and in the cellars the same nauseating scene was taking place—ten thousand pawing hands. . . .

The guard beside me had two wrist watches which had both stopped, one at seven o'clock and the other at three, presumably marking the hours of demise of two anonymous Germans. I had considerable difficulty in getting a glance at my own watch down in my coat pocket without the guard seeing it too, but fortunately I avoided putting his self-discipline to an acid test and discovered that it was past twelve o'clock. The half hour had become two. When the police officer finally returned, not out of the building but from a side street, he also carried a burden in his hand, a suitcase which, quickly and without comment, he threw on the back seat. Then he dismissed the soldier, who leaped out of the car, as if he had a lot to catch up with.

"We must go to the west, right out in the vicinity of the Stadium," said the police officer taking out a slip of paper with an address.

On the way I discovered that the events of the last week had changed the picture of Berlin totally. Whole streets were missing and characteristic buildings or spires, which one had previously been able to steer by, had completely disappeared. The police officer was an automobile fan and spoke many words in praise of the Mercedes, which pleased me greatly.

After a couple of hours' erratic driving, in and out among the ruins, we finally reached the address written on the police officer's paper, a very ordinary little workman's bungalow on a suburban road among numerous similar dwellings. There were several Russians in the road and two sentries posted outside the bungalow. I picked up my luggage and followed the police officer up the garden path to the front door which was instantly opened when he rang the bell. A lean face with sharp, almost birdlike features appeared, looking at us without enthusiasm. Hanging on a peg in the corridor there was a thick, black leather coat under a Russian service cap. The police officer moved swiftly to the door nearest the leather coat, and I followed but was waved back. The door closed behind the Russian, and I exchanged a brief look with the bird face which wore an expression of unmistakable loathing. I just had time to notice his neat, dark suit which looked unused rather than new, before he, too, disappeared into another room.

This time it was hardly ten minutes before the police officer returned, closing the door carefully behind him.

"It's as good as settled," he whispered in a confidential tone. "The commissar will handle your case, which I have explained to him in detail. He is just running through my report. Wait a moment and then go straight in there."

I waited a moment, knocked, then walked in.

The uneasiness which the sight of the leather coat in the corridor had wakened in me was accentuated when the owner of the coat looked up from a great sheaf of documents spread all over the dinner table. He had one of those unfeeling faces that always make me think of rum runners, racing drivers, football coaches and members of other exacting professions.

He sized me up as if I were a new make of car.

"American, I understand. How do you happen to be in Berlin?" he asked.

"I thought the police officer who brought me here had. . . ."

My supposition faded out, because I heard a car start up

outside and drive quickly away down the road. There had been no other cars parked out there when we arrived, and I suddenly understood a great deal. However, I forced my mind to concentrate on the matter in hand and gave him a brief explanation of my mission. I decided quickly to give him the real name of my chief as I had been instructed to do when I left Stockholm. It was then I discovered that necessity is the mother of linguists. Where I got stuck with my Russian, I filled out with German, of which the Russian officers all seemed to understand a little.

The commissar knew the ropes. He didn't start demanding documentation, but asked, "Have you anything to back up your story?"

"I have brought my transmitter and"—I thought of my Mercedes which the police officer was now happily driving around and was furious again, but I controlled myself and added—"my medicine chest."

It sounded utterly stupid. I felt that I might just as well have said my toothbrush.

"I'll go and get it, so that you can see for yourself," I hurriedly added, moving towards the door.

"No, no." The commissar started to fumble among the documents on the table. A brown leather handle appeared and proved to my wondering gaze to be part of a short thick whip. Maybe the business about the medicine chest hadn't sounded so stupid after all. The commissar whacked the whip down on the table. Immediately the door was opened and Bird-face stuck his head through.

"Fetch the American's luggage," ordered the commissar.

Bird-face looked at me. His loathing changed to vague wondering, then to doubt.

The commissar examined the transmitter professionally and put it aside.

"And this?" he asked, opening the medicine chest.

"Various drugs and chemicals dispatched to me from London," I said. "You can read the labels."

He couldn't.

"This one for instance?" he said, holding up a small package.

"Quick-acting poison, soluble in alcoholic drinks."

He put the package back quickly. "And this?" This time he only pointed.

"Probably poison, too." I bent over the chest. "Yes—preferably to be used in coffee."

He studied the package with professional interest. "Open it," he said.

I tore off the wrapper, interested myself because I had always put off ascertaining what was hidden behind the awe-inspiring labels. A few little white pills rolled out on the table. The commissar followed them with his eyes. When they stopped rolling, he tore a corner off one of the documents on the table, carefully picking up a pill in the paper between two fingers.

For a long time he stared in fascination at the little object, then he raised his eyes to me and asked confidentially, "Who were you supposed to liquidate?"

With a knowing smile on his lips he enjoyed my explanation that the poison was only intended for my own use in case of extreme emergency and that I had fortunately never needed it.

I pointed at all the other packages, bottles and tins. "The most important contents of the chest are meant to safeguard my personal health. Morphine tablets, antiseptics, vitamin tablets, cod-liver oil capsules. . . ."

I tried to explain to him that one of the reasons for the American victories could be found in the excellent American chemical industry which turned out countless preparations for safeguarding the health of the soldiers, whether in arctic regions, the tropics or Berlin. But he came from a state where everything has a secondary, secret and sinister purpose, and my explanation didn't make sense to him. He picked up his whip and walked up and down the room holding it behind his back. I became increasingly convinced that he had found an explanation that did make sense to him, namely that I had been sent to liquidate him personally, and that my show of frankness was only an exceptionally crafty tactical approach.

He swung the whip behind his back as if it were fighting a silent battle with the little white pills. Finally he stopped and said, "I will forward your case. I cannot make any decision on my own. The situation is still too unsettled."

He whacked the whip down on the untidy heaps of documents on the table, which immediately brought Bird-face back.

"The American will stay here for some hours. Attend to him," the commissar exclaimed, annoyed at the German because of his own broken German.

Bird-face and I went into a smaller room furnished by the barest necessities, a cupboard, a table and two chairs. He had undergone yet another change. His expression and manner had become that of an anxious host.

"You'll have to make do with what we've got," he said, waving his hand at one of the chairs. "If you wish to smoke the ashtray is there." He pointed at the floor and went on bitterly, "They wouldn't even let me keep an ashtray. They took everything into the garden and spent all night and this morning smashing it up before that guy in there arrived. They've turned the school down the road into a barracks. No one on this road is safe any more. . . . You're an American," he continued appealingly—and all of a sudden I understood the reason for his change of front—"Can't you do something for me? You're one of his allies. I've tried to talk with him myself, but either he can't or else he won't understand me. He's completely indifferent. He doesn't realize what it means. . . ."

"What?" I asked distractedly, because I was comparing his ashtrays with my Mercedes.

"I've just come back from a concentration camp," he said. "I'm a mechanic and an old social-democrat. I've had nothing to do with the whole thing. My last address should surely prove that. For two years I've been looking forward to seeing this place again, but when I finally got here there was no one at home. The neighbors say that my wife and daughter fled three weeks ago; nobody knows where. Instead that fellow with the leather coat arrived, and I know his type," he concluded scathingly.

There was a pause, during which I stealthily studied his thin, sharp features and the large hollows in the back of his neck just below the skull. There was no doubt that he spoke the truth.

"So those are the liberators," said Bird-face finally. "So far they have liberated me from everything my wife and I have worked and slaved for in order to get this house together. It will be interesting to see how many bricks will be left when we are liberated again by the British and then once more by your people," he added defiantly.

I felt sorry for this man, who seemed to be kicked by all masters. "There's not much hope," I said, "but I don't mind speaking to him."

Towards evening several Russian staff cars pulled up in front of the bungalow. From the window of the room where I was sitting I saw the Russian officers enter the house and go out again, driving away in their car. I got fed up with waiting, walked into the corridor and knocked on the door beside the leather coat.

"Shall I be moving off tonight?" I asked and then my glance fell on the transmitter and medicine chest I had forgotten to take with me when I last left the room. I thought they looked as if they had been tampered with.

"I have discussed your case with some staff officers. At the moment we have no possibility of contacting the American lines," the commissar said, poker-faced. "The situation is extremely changeable. As yet, we have hardly established contact with all our own divisions, scattered about in Berlin. But as soon as we get the whole matter cleared up"—whatever he meant by that —"your case will be rushed through. Until then you must consider yourself our guest. It will probably only be for a couple of days. You will be fetched and driven to the headquarters compound this evening."

We sized each other up. He held all the cards. I could only guess. Would any message about me ever be sent through to SHAEF?

As I was about to leave, I remembered my promise to Birdface.

"I don't know if you can be bothered to listen," I said, "but the man in this house has been a prisoner in a concentration camp. In his own way he has contributed to our victory. His nerves are out of order. Couldn't it be arranged that he——"

Impatiently the commissar waved me to silence. "I've heard enough of his moaning. He's not the only one whose nerves are out of order. Does he think the march on Berlin was a picnic? It's just like the Germans. They're moaning now, but only two years ago——"

"The man says he is a mechanic," I interrupted. "He claims that all his life he has been a—socialist." I just managed to get the right word at the last moment. "He has suffered a great deal for his beliefs."

"Socialist?" cried the commissar scandalized. He pointed his whip at the frail pinewood dinner table, the tiny sideboard, the two worn armchairs that made up the remnants of this little German workman's living room, typifying unpretentious taste and cheap mass production. "Are you trying to tell me that this is the home of a worker? Oh, no! The man is a bourgeois, and his surroundings are marked by fascistic and nazistic ideology."

The whip circled the room, pointing accusingly at all the little things that should have been there, but which the Russians had stolen, the clock, the radio, the pictures, the bric-a-brac, the ashtrays. . . . "Tell me, where in the world does a socialist live like this?" he demanded indignantly.

At any rate certainly not in Russia, I concluded silently and made up my mind that I wouldn't do Bird-face any good by pursuing the subject.

There was no light in the house and when, later that evening, I sat opposite Bird-face, sharing a bit of mildewed bread and a few cheese rinds by the gleam of a candle, I felt that I was home again, in the cellar in the everlasting darkness. Only Carl and Lili were missing. I wondered how they were getting on and then I thought of everything I had seen on this day of liberation, and suddenly I was unable to decide whether anybody had been liberated at all. I felt that I had landed in an unfortunate spot and idly considered leaving the house. But then I decided that, on the basis of the experiences I had already had, it might be wiser to work on the contact I had established with such difficulty rather than start all over again.

I was suddenly struck by an alarming thought: I might not be allowed to leave the house, even if I wanted to? But I banished the thought from my mind. The war was over, and the Russians were my allies.

"You're not eating anything," I said to Bird-face, trying to get my thoughts on a new track. He was actually pecking at the bread like a bird.

"Well, you see," he said. "I daren't. When you've starved every day for two years, you have to——"

He was interrupted by a piercing shriek from the darkness outside. It sounded as if it came from the neighboring house. I jumped up from my chair and looked out into the dark road. There was nothing to see, but the shrieks went on, increasing in volume. Someone else started to scream farther down the road. Then there were shrieks from another direction and yet another—as if all the inhabitants of the road had suddenly been seized with violent hysterics. A cold shiver ran down my back. The horror was so intense that I felt a sudden crazy urge to open the window and scream myself.

Instead I forced myself to look questioningly at my host, who was sitting with a tense listening expression on his gaunt face.

"The Bungalow Defense," he said, and his voice sounded as if he had bread in his mouth which he had forgotten to chew. "It was organized last night, when the Russians began to break into the houses. It's the only protection for the women. When the Russians come for them, everybody present starts screaming, and as soon as the people in the other houses hear it, they take up the scream. In that way they try to help each other. I'm told it's the only thing the Russians can't take, and that they usually slink out if people scream sufficiently loud and long."

We sat for a while listening. The darkness outside was quivering.

"It's the only joy I have felt for two years," said Bird-face, "that my wife and daughter had left before I came back."

About an hour later a car pulled up outside. The commissar came in and told me I was leaving. He escorted me out to the Russian army car, and saw that my transmitter and medicine chest were placed on the back seat. I was on the front seat beside the driver, a Russian corporal. I preferred to accept the commissar's attention as that of the polite host seeing his guest out, but as we drove off, I regretted that I had ever reported to my allies.

We drove for half an hour through green areas. The corporal at the wheel said nothing, leaving my imagination free to populate every bit of shrubbery we passed with creeping foot-steps and mauling hands.

Finally we came to a kind of barrier at the end of another suburban road. The barrier was lifted by invisible hands, and a moment later the car stopped in front of a house.

I was taken in and led through what seemed, in the dark,

to be a passageway. The corporal opened a door for me, put my luggage inside and disappeared, slamming the door behind him. I stood for a while by the transmitter and medicine chest, and then I tried the handle. The door was locked. That might, of course, be interpreted as protection. Then I felt my way through a pitch-dark room until I knocked against something. It was my only pleasant surprise that day—when I bent down and pressed on it, the long object felt considerably more comfortable to lie on than my boards back in the cellar.

# chapter ten

I woke up with a start under the impression that something was burning my cheek. I leaped out of bed and made for the window in order to escape. Here my sleepy and puzzled gaze was confronted—not as I had expected with suffocating smoke, crackling flames and crumpling walls—but with the pleasant green of the new spring foliage on hedges and trees. What I had thought to be an incendiary's sulphurous sting on my cheek had only been the warm fingers of the May-morning sun, flooding the room with brightness.

Hurriedly I completed the business of getting dressed—a small matter of straightening my tie and doing up my shoelaces —and slipped quietly into the adjoining room, eager to get the first impression of Russian hospitality.

I tiptoed across the shabbily carpeted floor, lowered myself gingerly into a large wing chair and proceeded to take in the room around me. The general atmosphere suggested ambitious middle-class fraying at the cuffs. All the same I had the feeling of an impecunious tourist, who has strayed into lodgings far beyond his means. Windows with unbroken panes, walls and ceilings unblemished by cracks or flaking plaster, chairs arranged in a set pattern suggesting comfort and relaxation—it was all so very different from what I had been used to, that I passed a half-embarrassed hand over the bristling stubbles on my chin and I was uncomfortably aware of the fact that my suit was crumpled and covered with spots.

But as I sank lower into the armchair, my inferior vagabond feeling gradually began to give way to a nagging uneasiness, an urgent desire to do something. For the first time in many months I had no programme for the day, nothing to watch and nothing to be wary of. I was beginning to feel bored. My throat was dry and rusty and I badly needed a drink. But I didn't suppose Russian hospitality included that kind of room service, and as the house was quiet as a tomb I gave up the idea with a regretful shrug.

I went back to the window and opened it. The morning sun laughed in my face as if to make light of all my sinister apprehensions. It was a wonderful morning. There were green gardens in front of decorative houses, and I felt convinced that I was somewhere in Grunewald, a district in the outer suburbs of Berlin. My surroundings suggested middle-class respectability. The houses were functional but uninspiring, solidly built to last.

I closed my eyes a moment and opened them again carefully as if to make sure that they had not been deceiving me. No—there were in fact no ruins; no gutted, smoking jungle with grotesquely twisted vines of sooty pipes and installations; no battered rusty bathtubs pathetically hanging like little stranded Arks of Noah high above the rubble.

I leaned out of the window and looked down to the end of the road, where the sight of a heavy barrier brought my pleasant reveries to an abrupt end. I inspected the road in the opposite direction, and once more my gaze was arrested by a similar heavy barrier. I gathered that the Russians had barricaded the section and were using it for billeting purposes. Right in the center of this enclosure they had placed their American guest. I sincerely hoped that it was with the intention of protecting him from harm.

The barriers were guarded by stocky Russian girl soldiers, dressed in rough blouses, short skirts, enormous boots and little sailor hats, precariously perched on their dark hair.

Seen at a distance with their broad backsides and impressive busts, they looked like uncanny hourglass-figured gnomes drawn forth from the bowels of the earth by an over eager sun. Between frantic gesticulations they hugged their carbines to ample bosoms with the loving tenderness of mothers nursing their babies. I looked at them despondently with nostalgic thoughts of other and lighter weapons which women of a different type had used with luck in bygone, almost forgotten days. One of the pocket amazons was standing in the doorway of a hastily erected guard hut, screaming into a telephone. Her razor-sharp voice left a deep gash in the morning stillness. Later I was to witness many similar examples of the deafening Russian approach to the telephone. Something seems to tell them that if only they yell good and loud into the magic black mouthpiece they will be heard in Moscow, no matter where they may be speaking from and regardless of trifling details such as getting the connection through at all.

As the morning wore on, the roads between the barriers began to swarm with activity. This gave me the opportunity of getting something I had always wanted—an undistorted view of a section of the Red Army.

My fascinating first impression was to be confirmed on many later occasions. The Russian army is composed of all the races, nationalities and types with which nature so abundantly strews the earth. Every physiognomy, every degree of intelligence from moronic apathy to the most refined intellectualism, is represented. Among the officers you find aristocratic faces with the unmistakable mark of good breeding; you see slim hands with carefully manicured fingernails and occasionally, when a well-pressed uniform containing an equally well-groomed Russian officer glides past, you find yourself inhaling the subtle fragrance of a good perfume.

This is of course the extreme case. The Russians did not march on Berlin in a cloud of perfume; nor were the machine guns trained on their objectives by sensitive manicured fingers. They were in the rough, capable hands of soldiers, whose square, thick-set frames and short, powerful legs suggested inexhaustible reserves of endurance and strength. Nevertheless the rank and file contained many different types—broad, round faces with blue eyes, but also narrow, yellow masks with prominent cheekbones and crooked slits for eyes. There were ruddy cheeks and pock-marked cheeks. There were easy going, childish peasant lads and inscrutable Orientals. It was like witnessing one of the busiest days of the Creation before there had been time for the first provisional sorting out.

In spite of all this contrast there were still a few common factors. The Russian army seemed to have a strong aversion to man's crowning glory in any style of hair and beard. Most of the soldiers were shaved clean down to the scalp. When it comes to making sacrifices and doing without, the Russians are unsurpassed at creating systems, uniformity and equality. Probably it was also a matter of hygienic considerations, for cleanliness and hygiene played an important part in the lives of the Russian soldiers. This fact was made vividly clear every time a Russian soldier opened his mouth in a smile and gave you an impressive view of the most elaborate artificial dentistry, wrought in silvery glittering amalgam. At first you were overwhelmed by the eerie quality of these metallic grins, and you wondered whether they were as artificial as the magnificent dentures that made them. But in time you got used to the naked polished skulls and the cold wintry gleam of the ghostlike smiles.

A third common characteristic of the Russian soldiers was

the childish pleasure they took in brightening up their dull brown uniforms that were a sad sight indeed for anybody with an eye for color. At this time it was the highest ambition of every Russian to own a black leather coat, and everyone from officers to buck privates tried his damnedest to organize one from the German adversaries. In the case of the privates, success brought joy of very short duration, their leather coats invariably being reorganized by the officers. In return, black S.S. breeches and high boots seemed to be exclusively reserved for the ranks. It often seemed as if entire S.S. regiments had been resurrected from the cold, damp mass-graves of the Russian plains and re-equipped with strutting new breeches and shiny black boots in order to score a delayed victory through a glorious tactical retreat to Berlin.

Around noon there was a polite knock on my door. I took this as a promising sign that the laws of hospitality would be observed, at any rate for the time being. A dapper little lieutenant entered and launched into an overwhelmingly friendly conversation. I have probably mentioned the fact that I had picked up enough Russian during my childhood in Riga to carry on a conversation of the more earthbound kind, and fortunately the lieutenant had not come to discuss problems of a higher intellectual plane—he merely wanted to escort me to lunch in the officers' mess. My spirits rose. This could only mean that my standing as an American officer had been accepted by the Russians.

The officers' mess consisted of two large adjoining rooms in one of the other houses. The tables were laid with the finest tablecloths and the most solid heirloom silver this occupied district had yielded. The menu, however, was less impressive: wheat grains boiled in water and beef cooked as a kind of hamburger. Still it tasted fine and for a long time I concentrated on my plate, stealing only an occasional surprised glance at the Russian officers whose table manners were remarkable. They heaped food high on their plates regardless of the numerous

197

little surplus helpings that piled up on the tablecloth around them. Then they swiftly chopped the meat into small pieces, stirred it all up in a mess with the cereal, and fairly shoveled it down with their forks.

I admired their dexterity and the terrific speed with which they cleaned up their plates, but as I find it easier to eat while observing my own rather more subdued national feeding habits, I plied my knife and fork with customary sedateness. I could not help noticing, however, that the Russians were sending sly glances my way, following every move of my utensils. All at once I experienced a growing alarm. What if the dawn of mutual Russo-American understanding should be held back by this difference in the use of knife and fork? It would be too obvious and impolite to change my pace in the middle of a meal, but I decided that thereafter the Russians should have no cause for complaint—at any rate as far as my table manners were concerned.

The following day I arrived at the mess all set to go, only to find twenty Russian officers decorously wielding knife and fork over their full but by no means overfilled plates. The heavy damask tablecloth dazzled my eyes with its unblemished whiteness. This was one of the few quiet victories I managed to chalk up for myself and Western culture during my stay with the Russians.

That first day, my new friend, the lieutenant, followed me back along the road to my house. He was rather touching in his effort to make it appear that his interest in me was devoid of any other motive than the spontaneous pleasure he derived from my company. When we arrived, he excused himself a moment and returned shortly afterwards with a big bundle under his arm. This bundle contained various articles of men's wear, the fruits of a lightning raid on some near-by wardrobe. He removed his tunic and spread the assorted garments out on the floor. Then he started trying on the different pieces of German civilian clothing, asking my opinion of each one.

I could see that this quick-change performance was designed to remove any suspicions I might harbor about his being my jailer. For how could I possibly think such a thing when he was putting on this civilian show for me? The uneasiness I had felt that morning returned, and all at once the May sun seemed deceptive and cold. But I resigned myself with the thought that, if I were a prisoner, I might as well settle down and enjoy a prisoner's privileges.

Accordingly I sat down in what was fast becoming the hub of my existence, the wing chair, and followed the lieutenant's fashion show with discerning interest. Finding no shirts in the bundle, he selected a gaudy pajama top and put it on. Next he fell for a fiery red tie, but he seemed to have considerable trouble fixing it under the pajama collar. I volunteered my help and initiated him in the profound mysteries of the Windsor knot. Should the Russians at any time claim the invention of this knot, or should they have already done so, let it hereby be disavowed.

The lieutenant—whose name was Smirnoff, and who was desperately homesick for some unpronounceable town in the Donets basin—was my faithful companion all the time I remained at Russian headquarters in Grunewald.

In time I came to loathe the sight of his perpetually beaming round face, jumping like a balloon at the end of his fiery red tie. He stuck to me like a shadow everywhere I went, and like most other people I prefer that my shadow be my own. But I believe that he found me a rare and interesting experience—not because I happened to be myself, but because he had suddenly been shut up in a cage with one of these strange Americans who sent all their automobiles, tanks and guns to the Russians, being afraid to go to war themselves. I often caught him staring at me in puzzled wonder.

Our conversation seldom strayed from such safe subjects as the last meal and the one to come, but occasionally mutual boredom drove us to an exchange of views on various principles. He was of a naturally happy disposition, though totally devoid of a sense of humor. He would go wholeheartedly for one thing at a time, but lacked the ability to compare it with another and, by way of contrast, find a third. If I had told him that this happens to be the main rule of Marxist dialectics upon which his whole upbringing must have been based, he would probably have been both puzzled and suspicious, taking my words as a particularly poisonous bit of enemy propaganda.

"Surely you know Roosevelt?" I asked Smirnoff one day.

Warily, as if afraid of walking into a trap, he admitted that he did.

"Well," I said, "wasn't Roosevelt an idealist?"

He fairly snapped the question out of my mouth. "So is Stalin!" he said quickly.

And it was always that way with those rare discussions that soared a little above food and physical needs. Questions were parried with some assertion or other—there was never a direct answer.

When I think back on it now, I understand my little lieutenant better. He was just a subordinate echo of a louder roar. As far as I can see there is not much difference between our discussions in Grunewald then and those exchanges of thought that have since taken place with the Russians in U.N. and elsewhere—except perhaps that the lieutenant and I had the sense to stop before we bored each other stiff.

On another occasion, when I was feeling thirsty, I asked him in fun, "Tell me, Smirnoff, everybody in Russia is equal. Right?. . . . Well, when everyone else has Vodka, why haven't you and I?"

The very next day two bottles of Vodka appeared on the table. I drank mine during a melancholy bout with homesickness. Smirnoff, who was endowed with youth's healthy contempt for the sobs of elderly sentimental fools, hastily withdrew without touching any.

The next day only his bottle was left on the table.

"Tell me, Smirnoff," I said again, "everyone in Russia is equal, huh? Why, then, have you got a whole bottle of Vodka, while I have none?"

The grave perplexities of this question seemed to stun him. Hesitatingly he handed me the bottle, while his brows became streaked with deep furrows of puzzled thought. I drank a toast to the communistic principles of equality, while he was still working on this strange problem that was far beyond the childish simplicity of the basic communism he had been taught.

One day the lieutenant organized a treasure hunt for my benefit. This was one of the favorite pastimes of the Russians in Grunewald. Armed with a watering can, you went around the gardens and sprinkled the soil. Sooner or later you would hit a spot where the water disappeared underground more quickly than usual. This was a sure sign that someone had been digging there recently. The Russians nosed like badger hounds into the fresh holes, and it paid off every time. Bundles, boxes and packages that showed unmistakable signs of having been hastily thrown together were hauled to the surface.

Eyes shining with the spirit of Christmas, the Russians tore the wrappings from their loot, and out poured silver forks and spoons, linen, rolled up paintings, clocks, ashtrays and plates as from a real treasure chest. The inhabitants of the houses—probably the women for the most part—must have been in a great hurry when they bundled their strange assortment of objects together to hide them from the approaching enemy. It looked as if they had made one wide sweep, brushing everything that happened to be standing on the tables, desks, bureaus, chests and washstands into the waiting sacks and boxes. Toy soldiers, cheap cuckoo clocks, children's shoes, photographs and trinkets were mixed up among the real valuables, and almost every treasure chest contained the most unexpected and unmentionable feminine garments.

But the reaction of the Russians to these treasure troves was just as unpredictable as their contents. Often they would be satisfied with a few pieces of ladies' underwear, a clock or some unusually cunning mechanical toy, and they would leave the silver alone. But in those days nothing went to waste. What the Russians left was stolen by the Germans and later re-stolen among themselves. Silver often changed hands three or four times, thus making it more than a theoretical chance that the rightful owner in time would be lucky enough to steal back his own property.

One day, when I had just returned from one of these treasure hunts with the lieutenant and once more stood looking dully out of the window at my limited world, I noticed a group of Russian privates engaged in a violent argument a little way down the road. Apparently two Russians were claiming the ownership of a pocket watch, and their pals were volubly and energetically taking sides. Their faces and gestures became increasingly aggressive, and I looked forward to seeing a real good brawl any moment.

Suddenly a Russian officer sauntered over towards the group. The men jumped to attention like puppets. With a weary gesture the officer beckoned the two leading characters of the drama before him. A brief exchange of opinions followed, but it was somewhat one-sided, the men's contribution being limited to "yes" and "no." Finally the officer took possession of the casus belli, the watch. He threw it casually up in the air as if tossing a coin, caught it and pushed it into his pocket without looking at it again. Then he turned and walked away.

For a moment the men remained frozen at attention. Then they slowly turned their heads and looked at the former owner of the watch. He was still standing with his hand out, staring down at his empty palm with a lost expression. Large tears were streaming down his round cheeks.

Just behind him there was a barbed-wire fence six feet high, which the Russians had erected between two houses. Suddenly I noticed how the quivering of his facial muscles increased. He started a slow rocking movement from one leg to the other. The movement gathered speed, until he suddenly jerked around and faced the barbed-wire fence. He threw his big hands on the top three or four strands and closed his fists around them with all his might. I could almost feel the pain of those sharp points digging into his palms and fingers. When he had a firm grip on the wire he flexed his legs and swung his body in an elegant arc over the fence. Landing heavily on his back on the other side, he buried his face in his torn hands, and lay there.

His pals stood speechless for a moment, before their petrified figures suddenly jumped to life. Roaring with laughter and dancing in front of the fence, they presented a strange spectacle. The lone figure on the other side raised a woebegone face and looked at them. His tears, mingled with the blood, had painted grotesque stripes down his cheeks. Then, to the increasing mirth of his comrades, he hid his face in his bleeding hands again.

# chapter eleven

But in time this unreal existence of part holiday part imprisonment came to an end. It happened after an eventful evening when the Russians had been having one of their private victory celebrations, and everyone in headquarters was rolling drunk, not from Vodka but from the German wine they had found in Berlin. This wine had been hoarded in great quantities by farsighted Germans, who wanted to give their American and British liberators a suitable welcome when they moved into Berlin. Now this liberation wine flowed freely, as intended, but down the wrong throats.

For this reason it did not surprise me that the two Russians who came to my room to fetch me the following morning spoke very little. They did their best to appear polite and pleasant, but words failed them. I knew that even the simplest thought would cause them considerable mental exertion after their violent nocturnal bout with the German wine. Therefore, when I had persuaded them to tell me that I was being transferred to the

Second Ukrainian Army headquarters, presumably situated nearer the center of Berlin, I lapsed into tactful silence.

I loaded all my earthly goods, the medicine chest and the suitcase with the radio transmitter, carefully into the back seat of an automobile parked outside the door. Then we drove away. At the end of the road a Russian girl soldier, the sailor hat bobbing on her thick black hair, raised the barrier and sent us a fierce parting look. I was on my way once more.

And let's hope it is the right way, I thought with some optimism, as I settled myself comfortably in the seat. So far I had no reason to doubt that my lenient imprisonment was just a slightly exaggerated form of Russian hospitality, where the host was over-anxious to see that his guest was not left alone for the slightest moment. A brief and formal interrogation at Second Army headquarters and then on to the American lines—a little way beyond that the return of the tired warrior. I closed my eyes and dreamily tried to picture a few details of this homecoming, but I got no further than the clean cool sheets, good well-pressed clothes, a clean shirt and three weeks in the bathtub.

The car bounced violently as we ran over a crater in the road, and I opened my eyes again. I realized that from the point of view of sight-seeing this trip did not promise too well. A dismal, gray desert of ruins stretched far away to all sides, and all I could see ahead of me was two close-cropped skulls, jerking in time with the vibrations of the battered old vehicle. The two Russians were obviously still suffering from a severe hang-over, and they had the pathetically comic appearance of Bad Examples in a documentary film, warning against the evil effects of alcohol. The thought made me thirsty. Involuntarily I moistened my lips, while my imagination conjured up a mirage in the barren waste of rubble—a Danish lunch with a dewy glass of icy cold schnapps as the main attraction. Once more I licked my lips. All that remained on my tongue was a sharp, bitter taste of soot, smoke and dust.

If I had not known we were in Berlin, I might easily have thought we were on the moon. The car crawled like a little, shiny black beetle round the incredible maze of shattered buildings. Springs and axles groaned ominously when we plowed through the shell holes or rattled over the tanklike tracks made by heavier vehicles in the rubble. The only thing that indicated the existence of other human beings in this desert were the makeshift Russian military signs, charred boards with directions scrawled in a hurried and often illegible hand. My thirst was getting steadily worse. The sun was scorching down on us, and the smell from the smoldering ruins closed in on us from all sides, suffocating and oppressive, filling the nostrils with a sickly stench.

The soldier behind the wheel was slowly regaining full consciousness. Our speed increased. Unfortunately the sporting instinct seemed to grow in him as the wine seeped out of his organism. He jammed his foot down on the accelerator without worrying about the condition of the road. We zigzagged crazily in and out among the ruins and shot around blind corners, only to come to a screaming halt a moment later, a few inches from a wall that blocked the road. Slap bang into reverse and off again, faster and faster. I clung to the seat in a hopeless effort to restrict the violent pounding of my skull on the roof, which seemed to be the only solid feature of the car. It soon developed into an exaggerated demonstration of driving round a corrugated Wall of Death. The two Russians were the enthusiastic daredevil performers and I an increasingly reluctant and pessimistic audience. Now and then, during one of my higher bounds into the air, I had the chance of getting a fix on our whereabouts. Finally I saw—standing as a feeble protest against the wide-spread desolation around us—a couple of large apartment blocks that formed a comparatively undamaged island in the flattened landscape of ruins. Immediately at the back of them I saw a large semicircular area, which I recognized as Tempelhof Airport.

I sank back in the seat, while a hope that started somewhere in the small of my back and slowly spread through all my limbs, made me smile with blissful expectation. Tempelhof Airport! Could this possibly mean that I would be flown over to the American side?

We covered the last lap with a hair-raising burst of speed and with a last tortured scream from the brakes stopped dead in the courtyard of one of the apartment blocks. A moment later the automobile seemed to collapse with a weary, sooty and evil-smelling sigh of relief coming out of the exhaust pipe. The two Russians looked triumphantly at each other, but then the enthusiasm died out of their eyes, the tensed muscles relaxed and the proud, intrepid hell drivers flopped back in motionless and disinterested apathy.

It seems as if the Russians have a special talent for going off into this loose-mouthed, bleary-eyed Zombie condition at will, apparently vegetating on the verge of life and death. This national characteristic has probably been perfected through several centuries of practicing one of the most difficult feats of all—the art of patiently waiting until you have forgotten what the hell it is you are waiting for.

For a long, long time nothing happened. And all of a sudden I felt the first icy touch of a gray mist that was to surround me during the rest of my stay with the Russians, a mist that finally threatened to drive me crazy—the feeling of being of no importance whatsoever, the feeling of being completely forgotten.

Time went very slowly. All around us there was a terrific bustling of disorganized activity. Officers and soldiers scurried past our little section of Sleepy Hollow without giving it as much as a single glance. It might as well not have been there at all. I tried to shake some life into my Russian companions. They seemed to look right through me with a glassy blue, vacant stare. I could read an all-embracing fatalism in the indifferent shrug of their shoulders. Destiny had landed them in this particular courtyard, and they might as well stay here as any other place.

It is an old ruse the Russians employ—forcing people to wait. It makes an opponent unsure of himself, fills him with a gnawing sense of inferiority and undermines his self-confidence. I recognized this well-known fact and firmly resolved that I would not let it get me down. Nevertheless the Russian strategy soon had its effect on me. Gone was that morning's dream of a triumphal flight back to the Americans. In its place I had a sneaking uncertainty as to where this journey would end.

The spiritual climate I had grown used to had undergone a noticeable change. Instead of my beaming little lieutenant there were now two Russians who made no effort to conceal the fact that they were armed guards. The warmish air of hospitality had suddenly changed to cold indifference, with black clouds of enmity banking up on the horizon.

The Russian who finally came up to the automobile fitted this new atmosphere very well. Not that his manner was anything but smooth and polite, but it was all put on for a purpose. There was a most obliging smile on his face, and I had a feeling that somebody else had put it there.

He was a Polish Jew and spoke fluent German. He introduced himself vaguely as an interpreter, but I did not for a moment doubt that he was a Russian policeman under orders to put out a few feelers to this suspicious-looking American with his radio and medicine chest. To carry out this task he had devised a plan of action which he no doubt considered both subtle and cunning. He never asked me a thing but took great pains to avoid the smallest hint of interrogation, chatting in a cozy and friendly way. He told me about a relative he had in America, probably to start me talking, but he showed no disappointment when I failed to rise to the bait. I circled carefully around the facts he already knew or could confirm without much trouble. I suppose he must have hoped all along that this gentle treatment would pay off in the end. But the treatment I got later indicated that I was a great disappointment to him.

In the meantime, while this camouflaged questioning went

on, he was prepared to do everything for me. He took me to the Russian canteen and gave me tea. When we had finished, my new Russian friend offered me a Mahorka. I hate tobacco in any form, but as everyone else in the canteen was smoking, I deemed it wiser to follow suit. Mahorka is a particularly vicious and torturous form of tobacco enjoyment. It consists of the whole plant, stalk, leaves, roots, soil and everything, run once through a grinder. The result looks like mahogany sawdust and is issued to the Russian soldiers by the pound. A suitable quantity of sawdust is rolled in a bit of newspaper, preferably of Russian origin. This is not for patriotic reasons, but because the Russian paper is of a very poor quality with a high wood content which makes it burn better than most.

After one careful puff at my Mahorka, I passed a discreet hand over my week-old stubble to see if my head was still where it should be. My Russian friend must have misunderstood this gesture, for he asked me whether I would like a haircut and shave. I accepted eagerly, and the interpreter took my arm in a friendly grip and led me out of the canteen.

We walked along the road until we came to a barbershop. It was locked up and a sign in the window said, "*Wird in zwei Tagen geöffnet.*" The interpreter hammered on the door and kicked it once or twice for good measure with his heavy boots. There was a sound of shuffling feet; the door was opened and a terrified German barber peered out. He opened his mouth to repeat the message on the window sign, but when the interpreter drew his revolver with a significant look, he closed it again and swallowed so hard that I could trace the lump all the way down his shrunken, skinny neck. We swept past him into the barbershop—the first time I had had the dangerous and demoralizing experience of belonging to an occupational force.

"My friend here wants a haircut and shave," the interpreter ordered.

The barber glanced at the revolver, shrugged in resignation and started elaborate preparations for a thorough haircut and beard-removing process. But not before he had carefully locked the door behind us. Apparently he was not keen on having more customers that day.

The Russian put his revolver down on a chair and brought out a wad of notes, flashing it at the barber. "We Russians pay for what we get. We are neither burglars nor robbers," he assured the barber, and there was an undertone to his voice that left the barber in no doubt as to what people the interpreter thought were mainly occupied with such dirty work.

The barber relieved his suppressed anger by violent attacks on my beard with his razor. I peered down at the flashing lethal weapon and sincerely wished that the two enemies would postpone their argument.

But presently professional zeal asserted itself and the defeated German was transformed into the eternal talkative barber.

While my hair flew under his snickering scissors, he told us how he had witnessed the Russian entry into Berlin. It appeared that he had held his ground, plying scissors and knives to the last and surrendering only when a dozen Russian soldiers charged his shop. But they had retreated in wild disorder, taking cover behind the door or around the corner, when they caught sight of the establishment's shiny hair-drying apparatus. Thereupon the barber, flattened up against the wall of the back room, had witnessed a brief but violent battle between the Russians and the drier. Withering Russian machine-gun fire had raked the shiny helmet, with its fearsome forks and threatening tongs, and finally brought it to silence. Then the Russians crept up on the awesome and dangerous enemy weapon, at first very cautiously and then more daringly. Finally they had rushed at it with their bare fists and had thrown it out on the sidewalk where it was smashed to atoms by the triumphant victors.

When we were through with the barber, who looked very skeptically at the German notes the Russian had pushed into his hand, we walked back to the courtyard.

My daredevil drivers of that morning had vanished together with their vehicle. In its place there was a large four-cylindered copy of a popular American sedan. The new driver, an Armenian with pale yellow skin and black curly hair down the back of his neck, was bending over the open hood. He had started the engine and put his ear down to the greasy, dirty pipes and leads, listening with an expression of the deepest rapture, as if its wheezy coughing was the most beautiful symphony.

My friend the interpreter left me in the hands of a private soldier of obvious Asiatic descent. A tall, stooping officer walked up to the car and sat down on the front seat. I noticed that his service cap fell down over his eyes and that all which supported it was his prominent ears. The Armenian got in behind the wheel, and the Asiatic motioned me to sit down on the back seat. The transmitter and the medicine chest were placed on either side of me, so that I was tightly sandwiched between them.

It was getting dark, and the fumes from the Russian gasolene, a gritty yellow fluid resembling diluted diesel oil, had a drowsying, almost narcotic, effect on me. My eyes were constantly watering, but every time I wanted to get my handkerchief out of my pocket, the Asiatic made a similar move for the machine gun in his lap. I noticed that we passed the same railway crossing twice and concluded that the Russians were just as ignorant of our whereabouts as I was.

The smell of gasolene grew steadily worse and was presently joined by a distinct smell of burning. This did not seem to bother my captors. The Armenian had already told me with some pride that this vehicle had blazed the trail from Stalingrad to Berlin, so I composed myself with the thought that after such a feat one had to make allowances for certain peculiarities. But suddenly the car reeled violently across the road, the smell of burning oil became more penetrating and finally the Armenian drew up. The officer came out of his doze and fired a volley of abuse at him. Then he flung out his hand and furiously gave the

Armenian some order. The latter started the car again and drove on, with the right-hand front wheel dragging along the uneven surface of the road. It was obvious that the front-wheel bearings were burned out, and only the Russian officer's desperation and anger kept the automobile going. As a motorist of long standing I shook my head at this folly, but then I remembered the Russian soldier who, in a similar state of despair, had mixed it up with a barbed-wire fence.

Naturally it was not long before the smell of burning rubber mingled with the smell of burning oil and the tire exploded with a loud bang.

Everyone got out of the car. Dusk had painted black violet shadows among the ruins—it was a barren, poisonous landscape, frozen in the grotesquely distorted convulsions of death. The Armenian opened the hood and looked at his beloved engine with grave concern. The officer and the Asiatic stared at me with hatred in their eyes, as if they thought I had sabotaged their vehicle. Then the officer directed me with a curt gesture to stand over against a half-collapsed wall. The Asiatic, who was facing me with his side to the wall, slipped the safety catch from his machine gun. The officer stepped behind me.

I tried to swallow but without success. I tried to say something, protest, tell them it was an outrage, that I was an American, one of their allies, but not a sound came from my lips. In the dusk I could just see the Asiatic's eyes gleaming behind slanting lids that looked like narrow, menacing firing slots. I did not obey the officer's command. I stood quite still— probably because I just could not move. Everything had happened so quickly, my fall from Russian grace had been so sudden that I was practically paralyzed by the shock.

For a dreadful moment the three of us remained standing there, loaded with tension to the point of bursting. I glared stiffly at the Asiatic's eyes, and they in turn seemed to look dispassionately through me, watching the officer who stood behind me. I ceased being a living organism then! I had neither weight nor solid form any more; I was nothing but a stiff glare, frozen in panic, directed against an unfeeling machine that was about to exterminate me. It was a moment that defied the normal conception of time. It was like a whole period of my life.

At last I saw the tense expression die away from the Asiatic's eyes. His hand relaxed on the gun. I heard footsteps behind me, and an exclamation like an angry curse, and then somebody walked away. Still I did not move. My face felt swollen and numb as after an anesthetic. The Asiatic tucked his gun in his belt with a look of complete indifference. My body began to function once more. There was a throbbing at my temples. I went over to the automobile and sat down heavily on the running board.

I had not been shot after all, and I suppose I cannot really say whether the Russians had intended to kill me there in that grim valley of death, as a last delayed victim of the Allied cause—at any rate in that war. But sitting there on the running board in the dusk of evening I realized that I had avoided some irrevocable fate by pretending to be calm, indifferent and cold-blooded—which was very far from what I really felt, but which must nevertheless have been convincing enough to make them respect me. That was the only explanation I could think of. I realized that I was on the run again and once more among enemies, and that calmness, cold-bloodedness and indifference were the only defense I had. I hoped that I could mobilize these weapons before it was too late.

An hour later the officer returned with a small Opel runabout. Apparently it had belonged to some German tradesman, for the back seat had been removed. I crawled in and sat down on the floor with the Asiatic, and we continued our journey. By now it was pitch black outside. We came to a highway where we encountered mile-long convoys of tanks. I noticed with sinking spirits that they were heading towards Berlin.

We left the highway, and at about ten P.M. we drove up in

front of a house in a comparatively undamaged district right on the perimeter of Berlin. Over the front door I could just make out the contours of a bull's head, and in my exhausted and bewildered condition I toyed for a moment with the crazy idea of a cozy country inn. I was pushed through the door and crashed up against a counter that stretched across the room. On the counter a sleepy oil lamp threw an enormous black shadow on the white tiles of the wall. I ran my eyes along the edges of the shadow and saw a row of black iron hooks, fixed with their barbs pointing upwards in the spaces between the tiles. I gave up the idea of a country inn on the spot and settled for an up-to-date, scientific and hygienic torture chamber.

A head appeared over the counter and was followed by a figure in a dirty, crumpled uniform. The soldier looked at me sleepily. Then he opened his mouth in a wide and unconcerned yawn, looking in distraction at his right hand that was holding on to one corner of a large, dirty sack. A look of bewilderment passed over his dull features. Then he dropped the sack and shuffled across the stone floor to the back of the room, where some steps led the way up to a door. All of a sudden I realized that I was in a butcher shop.

A moment later the sleepy guard returned with two uniformed Russians. One had an intelligent but cunning face, with eyes red-rimmed through lack of sleep or too much drink. He listened a moment to the officer who had brought me, and then abruptly dismissed him. He seated himself on the counter, and looked at me with an expression of intense boredom. The other Russian loomed out of the shadow cast by the lamp like a very passable imitation of the once-so-popular King Kong. He had the general appearance of one of those big silent so-you-won't-talk guys used in gangster films to draw quick confessions from reluctant victims. He was bald as a coot, and his head was shaped like a slightly rounded pyramid. A massive jaw was the base from which the lines of his face stretched upwards at different angles, until—for no apparent purpose—they met at the point where other people are presumed to have the center of their thought.

"Papers!" said the red-eyed officer laconically and lit a cigarette.

I explained my special circumstances. I handed him the passport I had used in Germany, but told him it was a forgery made in London. Finally I gave him my O.S.S. number, telling him that he could verify it by getting in touch with the American forces.

Red Eyes casually thumbed through the pages of my passport. Then he threw it on the counter and nodded to King Kong. The latter grabbed my lapels in both giant paws and prepared to give me a thorough frisking.

"You have no right to do this. I'm an American officer. You can confirm that anytime," I shouted angrily and struck at King Kong's hand. He removed it willingly enough, but a second later I got it back with a resounding smack on the jaw.

"Who says you are telling the truth?" asked Red Eyes in a disinterested tone. "Who says you're not a filthy S.S. bastard?" He had not even raised his eyes when King Kong hit me.

My head was still ringing with the blow. I supported myself against the counter. "If you will contact the American authorities, you will be able to verify my statement," I repeated for the third time.

I realized how ridiculous my words sounded in these surroundings, but it was my only chance. In the meantime King Kong had ripped off my coat and was busy running through the pockets.

"The Americans will vouch for anybody," said Red Eyes drily. "Lots of Nazi swine have run over to their side. The Americans greet them with open arms. They have no idea of fighting a war themselves, and now they want the Nazis to teach them. American officer!"

He jumped down from the counter and walked over to kick my suitcase and medicine chest inquisitively with his foot. Once more I tried to tell him that they had been my weapons in my own little fight for his and for the Allied cause in Berlin.

He opened the medicine chest and took out a couple of the tins. He tried to read the labels, shook the tins, opened them and sniffed at their contents. Then, losing interest in the medicine chest, he turned his attention to the radio transmitter. He put on the earphones and twisted the knobs, listening with a strained expression as if he were hot on the trail of some dark secret. Finally he straightened and gave me a look that was both triumphant and accusing.

"You are not an American officer! You are a spy! You have slipped through the Russian lines to find out our strength. Your methods are as dirty as your intentions—poison, narcotics —the sneaky weapons of an assassin!"

I wanted to interrupt him, but he dismissed me with a wave of his hand.

"You will be given the opportunity of explaining yourself," he said curtly. He gave an order to King Kong, who at the moment was busy on my jacket, and went quickly to the back room, closing the door behind him.

I had to hand it to King Kong. He was an expert. With practised skill he examined every possibility of secret hiding places in my clothes. He ripped out the lining of my overcoat and jacket and split the soles of my shoes with a knife. Finally, when he had been through everything and found nothing, he looked at me for a moment with an expression akin to reluctant approval—as one efficient gangster might show a colleague his professional admiration. Then his face returned to its former primeval inscrutability. He motioned me to remove my collar and tie, and these were bundled into my scarf together with my fountain pen and the old twenty-mark gold coins I had used as identification among my contacts in Berlin. The bundle was thrown among my other possessions. Then he ordered me to take the laces out of my shoes.

I had never before realized how large a part of one's

dignity is attached to these small, fragile objects. While you still have them you are a free man with at least the theoretical possibility of a springy step and erect carriage. Without them you become a sloppy individual already branded with the mark of the slave.

King Kong took the oil lamp and put it down beside a trap door in the floor. The soldier retreated to the farthest corner of the room as King Kong pulled open the trap door and motioned me to go on down ahead of him. This was the only polite gesture I ever got out of him.

The stone steps were damp and slippery. A warm, putrid stench from below made me hold my breath. Everything in me that was still civilized revolted against going into this cellar, where apparently some store of meat from the butcher shop must have been in the process of decaying for a long time.

I stopped short, but King Kong who was right behind me with the lamp pushed me in the back. I stumbled down the next two steps, and in the flickering light from the lamp I could see where the vile stench came from. The shelves of the butcher's cellar were crammed—not with meat as I had expected—but with human flesh, some of it living and the rest already dissolving in putrescence.

On the wooden shelves a dozen men or so were bundled together. Some sat on the edges of the shelves looking dully at the light from the oil lamp, while others lay motionless. The floor was covered with an indescribable sludge and it was from this that the filthy stench of diarrhea rose to my nostrils. Back in Berlin former concentration camp prisoners had described their stinking barracks so often that my present surroundings seemed almost familiar. The only thing that was out of line with the general atmosphere—so much in fact that it appeared profanely absurd—was the fact that these prisoners, far from being ragged, were dressed in clothes which, though crumpled and dirty now, would have been worthy examples of the finest tailoring a few days before.

But this thought did not occupy my mind for more than a split second. As I stood there wide-eyed at all this human debasement and indignity, I was filled with fury and disgust that coursed through my veins like a scalding wave. I flung myself around, shoved King Kong out of the way so that his lamp clattered against the wall and scrambled wildly up the slimy stone steps.

Once more in the butcher shop, I ran across the stone floor, pressed my back against the wall and started shouting a stream of invectives in all the languages I could think of. It was as if the nauseating stench, lying like a film across my mouth and nostrils, influenced my Russian vocabulary and gave it venom it never had before or since. I stamped my feet on the floor, I cursed and shouted, I hammered my fists against the wall. I demanded my rights. I told them I was a personal friend of General Eisenhower. I swore that I would see to it that every Russian in this house and for miles around was hung. I disclosed my very close connection with Roosevelt. I boasted of mythical heroic deeds in Berlin. I warned King Kong and Red Eyes, who had been drawn out of his back-room lair by the noise, of the international complications that would arise when this scandal was published in the world press. I pointed with a shaky but menacing finger at the trap door and declared that when Maisky in London heard of this, it would only be a matter of very few days before they would be thrown down there themselves and left to rot in their own filth.

Red Eyes stared at me coldly. He was obviously trying to make up his mind whether I was bluffing. But all the big names I threw at him, especially Maisky's—which by some lucky chance I had happened to remember—seemed to make quite an impression on him. For a moment the fear that haunts every Russian—the fear of responsibility, the fear of having to make an independent decision, which may be disapproved of in higher places—fought with his honest conviction that I was a common spy who ought to be wiped out. But this fight brought uncertainty. After all, there might be just a faint possibility that I was telling the truth—or part of it. He wavered; then he motioned King Kong to close the trap door. He snatched the dirty sack from the guard who had intended to use it as bedding and flung it under the counter. Then he gave me an angry nod, which I took as a sign that I could camp down on the sack instead of joining the prisoners in the cellar.

Later, when both Red Eyes and King Kong had disappeared into the back room from where I could hear them phoning to every corner of the earth—except, I presumed, the West—I slipped quietly over to my medicine chest and opened it. The guard followed me with his eyes but said nothing. He must either have been hypnotized by my nerve, or else he just didn't give a damn. I got out a tin of morphine tablets, swallowed two of them, and crawled as far down in the sack as I could get.

When I woke up the next morning, the shop was already full of customers. There was a steady stream of well-groomed, eager-beaver Russian officers running in and out of the back room. Most of them paused for a moment to study the American on the sack with inquisitive interest. I could tell by their faces that they were not particularly impressed. At first I found it unpleasant to be forced to display my humiliation in public. But I pulled myself together and raised my head from the pillory to meet the inquisitive stares with the same expression of dignified contempt the lion in the zoo used to wear when, in my childhood days, I went to visit him on Sunday afternoons.

In the meantime I was busy making new shoelaces from threads I had pulled out of the sack. When I had finished, I sat with my back against the counter, staring into space with the heavy mantle of Job around my shoulders.

After a couple of hours the guard brought me a plate of boiled wheat grains and chunks of meat. There was also a hot cup of tea to wash the food down. It tasted fine. I had barely finished when the guard returned to take me out for exercise.

He led me outside and along a muddy trampled path, hedged in with barbed wire, to some foul-smelling latrines behind the house. The stench was so strong and the scenery so repulsive that I just could not do what the guard expected of me.

When we returned to the butcher shop, there was a Dodge truck parked in front of the door. It had been backed right up to the entrance with the backboard down, so that you could get directly from the shop into the truck. A small group of soldiers was busy loading it with captives from the cellar. As is customary when prisoners are transferred from one place to another, there was a good deal of unnecessary screaming and shouting. The scene had the easygoing informality of cattle transport. Most of the prisoners were so weak that they could hardly walk. One of them was literally dragged into the truck by his comrades. Again I was struck by the distinguished appearance which they had somehow retained even in the depths of their terrible degradation.

Finally I was pushed into the truck and my luggage thrown after me. The backboard was raised and a soldier, armed with a machine gun, jumped up, slipped the safety catch from his weapon and sat down facing us. The truck drove off and in a short while we hit the highway, where we joined a convoy of five or six other trucks, each with a guard on the backboard like a sort of reversed figurehead. I started a whispering conversation with the prisoner who had spoken Russian. He was a tall gray-haired man with marked features and intelligent eyes.

"Who are you?" I whispered, trying not to move my lips.

"We were in the Italian Embassy. Captured in Berlin during the capitulation. We are——"

"Shut up!" roared the guard and rattled ominously with his gun.

We drove on in silence.

It took some time before I could co-ordinate my senses to anything resembling methodical thought. But eventually I realized that we must be traveling along the highway to the

East Prussian town of Kustrin. I was heading east! We were sneaking along very slowly way over on the right-hand side of the road to make room for mile-long Russian tank convoys moving in the opposite direction. I had been shanghaied in on one of the greatest military processions that have ever taken place. In the fields by the side of the road several hundred thousand spectators were gathered to watch the passing columns of steel—not with enthusiasm but with the weariest apathy. They were the defeated German army, dirty and ragged, watching the conqueror's display of seemingly inexhaustible reserves. Now prisoners of war, they were going the same way as I was. For a moment I shook my head at this fantastic thought. My enemies were now my fellow sufferers, my allies my enemies. That one quick mental somersault showed me something which a great many people spent three years getting wise to.

It was late afternoon by the time we reached a pass between some heaps of rubble that were once the suburbs of Kustrin. The entire town had been shelled to bits during the Russian crossing of the Oder. On the edge of this destruction we ran into a traffic jam of fantastic dimensions. West-going trucks and armored cars were stuck fender to fender in an unbroken line as far as the eye could see. Staff cars had tried to find a loophole in the chaos only to be helplessly wedged in between the larger vehicles.

A few erratic maneuvers from our driver quickly put our truck in the same position. The traffic jam was buzzing with excitement. Bewildered drivers, officers and private soldiers dashed in and out among the vehicles, shouting and gesticulating. The atmosphere was saturated with irritation. Impotent commands and curses sizzled through the air, interspersed with the crash of cars that collided while trying to get out of the mess.

I sat lethargically on the floor of the truck, watching this immense administrative snafu. Naturally the idea of escaping had been at the back of my mind ever since I realized which way I was going, but so far I had not seen the slightest possibility of getting away with it. I was surrounded by keen and zealous reserves of the Russian army, and it would take less than no time to concentrate the collective fire of a whole tank division on my all-too-conspicuous person if I tried to make a run for it. And should I, dressed in a thick overcoat and brown fedora, succeed in sneaking through this wall of uniforms, I would come up against a new wall, consisting of German P.O.W.'s. Once captured there, I could neither talk nor bluff my way out, even if I could have proved that I had been Roosevelt's favorite son.

In the midst of these despondent reflections on my hopeless situation a natural physical urge forced me to think of something more concrete. I had not been able to do what was expected of me in the back yard of the butcher shop, but now the urge became increasingly strong.

I told the guard, who sat dangling his legs over the backboard, that my situation was critical. He looked suspiciously at me, but made a gesture with his gun which I took as permission to carry on. I stepped over the Italians on the floor and jumped down. It was wonderful to stretch my legs again. Firm ground under my feet—it was enough to give me renewed courage.

The guard watched every move I made. My natural modesty forbade me perform in front of such an attentive audience who seemed afraid to miss the slightest detail. I gave him a sheepish grin and retreated down the side of the truck. He poked his head around the corner and kept looking. I turned and faced the back wheel.

I was halfway through when there was a terrific crash behind me followed by the tinkling sound of breaking glass. I turned around in alarm and saw a big truck that had backed into another. The drivers shot out of their respective cabs and started a violent argument. I resumed my affairs at the back wheel, taking my time about it. It was a real good and thorough argument between the two men, who knew every curse worth knowing in the Russian language. One driver advised the other to do certain detailed but unprintable things to his mother, while the other retaliated with similar suggestions with regard to his opponent's grandmother. In this way they gradually covered the entire distaff side of their respective ancestors.

I glanced in the direction of my guard. He was leaning forward on the backboard with his half open mouth making scarcely perceptible movements, as if he were trying to memorize the choicest curses of the two drivers. He looked like a man who is completely engrossed in a prize fight.

Without having any clear idea of what I was doing and without any plan, but guided by some inexplicable instinct, I started walking slowly backwards, drifting diagonally away from the side of the truck. The sheepish grin I had sent the guard earlier re-appeared on my face of its own accord. I had no idea where I was going, but some strong power was drawing me backwards. In a flash I saw that I was about to collide with an officer who was hurrying to the latest crash.

Suddenly the whole situation appeared before me like a movie still in which I was both performer and spectator: The two angry drivers in their oil-stained uniforms, leaning aggressively towards each other with every muscle strained; the officer who shouted a furious command in their faces; my open-mouthed guard attentively leaning forward; and myself, wearing a sheepish smile and slowly moving backwards, not because I knew where to go, but probably because I instinctively hoped there might be some way out.

My somnambulistic reversing was rudely interrupted when my shoulder hit something sharp-edged and hard. In a fraction of a second I made sure that what I had bumped into really was—what I had known instinctively it would be—the backboard of a truck that had its nose pointed the right way, facing west. Quickly I swung my body over the backboard and threw myself flat on the floor with my face pressed down into some sack that smelled of earth and half-rotten vegetables.

For a long time I lay there with my face against the rough sacking, trying to get calmed down. My heart was hammering so loud that I was afraid they would hear it outside. Any moment I expected to feel the muzzle of a gun dig into me, followed by a command that gave me the choice of two equally unpleasant evils.

But nothing happened. The buzz of excitement, the shouted commands and the curses continued outside. I crawled as far into the truck as I could get. After a very long time I heard some engines being started. I raised my head carefully, and in the darkness I could just see the convoy that had brought me beginning to move off slowly. There was no indication that they missed me. With perspiration streaming down my face and my nails digging into my palms from fear and excitement, I saw them disappear among the unending rows of vehicles. They were headed east—towards the boundless desert and the eternal winds.

The convoy carried away my medicine chest, my transmitter and my well-worn overcoat which I had taken off before leaving the truck. The empty shell of a secret agent was on its way eastwards. I hastily put a hand in my inside pocket. Thank heaven, my forged passport was still there. I wondered where it would get me now. While I was still thinking about it, my new convoy moved off. My eyelids grew heavy and soon I fell asleep.

# chapter twelve

A morphine tablet from the previous night was still doing its merciful work, shielding me in a deep darkness, where there were neither Russians creeping around with machine guns, nor bright suns following their inexorable path from east to west. Subsequently my return to reality was all the more painful. There was a bump from the truck, and I landed in a world of hard facts like a parachute jumper who has touched down clumsily and ended up flat on his face in a turnip patch. The stench of half-rotten vegetables coming from the sacks told me only too clearly where I was. I raised myself reluctantly and peered out over the backboard.

The convoy had stopped. In the light of the powerful head lamps I saw Russian soldiers staggering around with equipment, weapons and odd bundles. The general bustle of activity suggested a longer stay. I might as well get it over and done with right away!

I swung myself down over the backboard and took a quick

look around. I hadn't much time to make up my mind. It was a matter of finding the convoy commanding officer as quickly as possible. First impressions are decisive. I preferred to meet him as a free man rather than a prisoner with a Russian machine gun in my back.

The convoy had pulled up in the middle of a narrow street in some German small town. I stepped on to the sidewalk, pushed my hands in my pockets and leaning slightly forward like a man who is abroad on urgent business, quickly covered the few paces to the head of the convoy. A group of officers were engaged in conversation by the front vehicle. After a quick glance at their uniforms I decided to make for a tall colonel in a long unbuttoned military coat. He was standing with one foot on the car bumper and seemed to be issuing some orders which he accentuated with small energetic whacks of one index finger on his open palm. I didn't like the look of those little abrupt cuts that seemed to sever any possibility of discussion. But there was no other way out. I took a deep breath, wound myself up as if for some arduous athletic effort and walked with a spring in my step into the full light from the headlamps.

"American officer!" I said, and tried to make my heels click with military precision. "On my way to the American lines. Attached to your convoy for futher transport!" I found that my voice actually sounded firm, almost as if I were quoting an order from some high and impressive Russian headquarters.

The colonel's finger, halfway through its downward chopping movement, hovered in mid-air. His amazed expression reflected only too clearly the suspicious person who had suddenly loomed out of the darkness: an unshaven tramp in dirty clothes and with a crumpled hat in his hand. He sniffed and screwed up his nose. Obviously my smell did not appeal to him any more than my appearance. He took a few paces back. Slowly his amazed expression faded. His eyes hardened and he opened his mouth to begin a stream of questions. It was imperative for me to retain my lead.

"Reporting, according to instructions, my return from secret mission behind German lines. I'm prepared to give you my O.S.S. rank and number."

I might as well have said Y.M.C.A. for all the recognition the initials aroused in the colonel. "Identity papers?" he demanded. "Transport order?"

"Only this," I said and handed him my threadbare passport.

He thumbed through the pages. His fingers were like small flabby cushions, thick at the roots and tapering in a repulsive way towards the nails. He leaned over and held the passport under the head lamps.

"There is no existing precedence for a case like yours," he finally said, changing to broken German, probably because he had seen the German stamps in the passport. "The Americans have not as yet moved into Berlin, and we have no means of contacting them." His index finger landed with a sharp crack on the passport. At the same time he turned his head with a curt conclusive movement.

When his eyes came back to me again the expression in them told me that he was both annoyed and surprised that the crack of his finger hadn't removed both me and my tedious problem from his vicinity.

"You must consider yourself detained until further notice," he said at length, relieved to have found a regulation under which I could be placed.

"But I must insist that you respect my rank as officer," I replied firmly. I was prepared for arrest. The most important thing was to assert my position as an American officer.

The colonel tried to button his long coat across his protruding stomach but gave it up. He waved the other officers closer. They formed a huddle around me. Then he sauntered over to the next vehicle of the convoy, where another Russian officer, a captain, as far as I could see, was bending over one of the head lamps, checking something off on a piece of paper. Even

229

if you took the captain's strained attitude into consideration, his unproportionately large backside that threatened to burst the tight uniform pants, still seemed obscenely feminine.

The colonel gave him a gentle pat on the shoulder. The captain stayed in the same position, barely turning his head. The colonel whispered something in his ear. The captain reached for the passport and went through it page by page. When he had finished, he gave it back to the colonel and shook his head. The colonel waved a hand in explanation, but the other seemed hard to convince. He spoke agitatedly and at length. Finally he straightened up, and I observed that this made no apparent difference to the remarkable dimensions of his behind.

Keeping up a steady stream of words, he waved the paper in his hand under the colonel's nose. The colonel laid a soothing hand on his arm, but couldn't get a word in edgewise. The officers around me followed the incident without betraying any emotion, but there was a sense of strain in the atmosphere, and I guessed that this exchange of opinions involved greater stakes than my own wretched person.

Then suddenly, interrupting the captain's agitated flow of words, the colonel's index finger thudded decisively down on my passport, while he shouted something that to my ears sounded like a command. The captain dried up. His excitement abated as quickly as it had been aroused. He shrugged and turned his head away—like an actor who, having put his heart into a spirited soliloquy before an unfeeling audience, walks out on it.

They both sauntered over to me. The captain didn't say a word but flashed me a stabbing look which, however, glanced off like a blade that has been dulled with too frequent use. There were small beads of perspiration under his service cap. In the strong light his face looked loose, puffy and yellow, as if it had been powdered. It strengthened my impression of a ham actor losing his grip and at heart gravely worried about his career.

"We are agreed to accept you for what you claim to be until further notice," said the colonel. "I trust you realize the consequences if you have tried to deceive us," he added impassionately.

The captain made a face which was quite superfluous. I knew exactly how I stood with him.

Two Russian soldiers escorted me down the main street of the little town. We didn't meet a single civilian and only saw lights in those houses that the Russians had commandeered for the night.

We turned down a side street and came to a neat, middle-class house. One of the sentries shot away the front door lock with his machine gun, as unhesitatingly and matter-of-factly as others might use a key, whereupon he entered, switched on the lights and opened the doors of all the rooms. He went upstairs and repeated the same process. Then he came down again and beckoned his comrade and me to come inside.

I was shown to a bedroom where I collapsed in exhaustion on the ready-made bed. The two soldiers sat down in the dining room next door and took some bread out of their packs. They ate silently and methodically but without the slightest indication that the meal afforded them any pleasure. I lay on the bed gazing at the ceiling. It might have been worse, I thought.

I woke up next morning to the same scene, the only difference being that the sentry was sleeping, his head cradled in his arms. The electric light was still burning brightly. I sat up on the edge of the bed and sent the now-vigilant sentry a timid morning smile to tell him that I was ready for my morning coffee. He didn't make the slightest response.

Shortly after noon the convoy resumed its journey. I was wedged in beside the colonel in the front seat of a comparatively new but already outworn Studebaker, that rattled and shook as if all its inner components were fighting each other. I kept a watchful eye on the sun and saw to my relief that we were still going west.

We passed through a small glade, where a lot of large trucks had been parked, decked with flowers, garlands, green foliage and red flags. The flowers drooped their heads and the garlands were faded and crumpled. The Russian drivers were lying just off the edge of the road, sleeping with their caps over their faces. There were bottles scattered around in the grass. The scene was like a huge fraternity picnic, where the participants have hit the bottle a bit too hard and have passed out.

I looked questioningly at the colonel.

"Participants in one of our victory parades," he grunted as if he were afraid to reveal too much. I had to be content that we were at least on speaking terms.

A little while later we went through a long row of timber erections, framing the road like portals. They were triumphal arches but of the cheapest variety, constructed from odd materials at hand in the ruins, charred boards and beams knocked together in great haste. The décor varied with each of the arches, but the subject was always the same: enormous glamourized pictures of Stalin and the better-known Russian generals. In the center of every triumphal arch there was a giant painted clock that showed the exact time of the day when Berlin had fallen into Russian hands.

Small groups of Germans studied the inscriptions painted with black poster lettering on gray sacking and phrased in both Russian and German. You could almost see a professional interest in the faces of the spectators. Here at last was something in their new masters which they could understand: giant posters, slogans, propaganda, idolatry. They must have felt as if a new circus had come to town.

We drove at last into the eastern suburbs of Berlin, and never had the hideous ruined German capital appeared more beautiful to me. We came to a barrier that was raised by a small, broad-bosomed Russian amazon and drove into a Russian compound like the one I had known at Grunewald, only this one consisted of three-story suburban houses. I sighed with relief. It was like coming home after a long and perilous journey. The colonel signaled me to jump down.

"You must remain here until we have verified your statement," he said in his dispassionate voice. There was no sympathy in his cold blue eyes, but on the other hand there was no enmity either. I was just an administrative case for forwarding, and his sole concern was to find the appropriate stamp. My only consolation was that I had seen him with my own eyes fighting to hang on to his little case. I hoped that he would fight again if anyone tried to take it away from him.

"I shall give you two reliable men as sentries—for your own sake, too," he added inadvertently looking down the convoy. I followed his gaze and saw the tight seat of a pair of black pants edging with some difficulty out of a truck door. "You can get in touch with me at all times through your guards. If you have any complaints with regard to your stay here, let me know. See you later," he concluded, and turned around on his heel.

I thought I recognized those tight, black pants, as they waddled off in the colonel's wake. Then I realized that they belonged to my adversary of the previous evening, the perspiring captain.

I felt quite relieved, when my two guards came sauntering over to me. One of them, a tall, fair country lad, looked searchingly around—like a hotel porter wondering why the guest has no luggage. The other, a small, dark nimble man with a funny, puckered, simian face, gave his pal an impatient shove, whereupon all three of us crossed the road and entered one of the three-storied houses. A foul stench met me on the stairs. The floor of the first story was under water, and it was from this flood that the stench arose. I began to have unpleasant apprehensions about my new apartment.

The little dark guy grinned and balanced across the boards that formed a makeshift bridge to the next flight. He pointed at a door and shouted some word to his comrade. The country lad pinched his broad nose and repeated the word with a snigger. Suddenly I understood both the word and the connection. The water came from the toilets of the house, situated on the intermediate landings and apparently apt to overflow.

I repeated the word with my fingers pinching my nose. Both the Russians grinned broadly in spontaneous admiration of my unexpected familiarity with the darkest and most evil-smelling pits of the Russian language. The ice was broken.

We went into the top apartment, consisting of a little hall that led directly into the sitting room which contained, among other things, a piano. To the right of this was the bedroom and to the left the kitchen.

The Russians remained in the hall while I inspected my new environment. Finally I threw my hat on the sofa as an indication that I had taken possession of the sitting room. The Russians took turns at fetching their weapons, equipment and numerous bundles from the trucks downstairs. They dragged it all into the bedroom and started building an artistic bivouac on and around the wide double bed.

I opened the window, as one always does upon arrival at a new hotel. The spring air flowed into the room, replacing the damp, stagnant, moldy atmosphere with a light breeze smelling of earth, wet grass and flowers. The evening was perfectly still. The sky hovered like an enormous bright dome above an almost lifeless landscape. I had a very fine view, first of a large green lawn, that started just below the window and stretched across to a big gray building surrounded by a high wall. Then there were long rows of gutted skeleton houses and finally more green areas, small glades and fields fading away on the horizon. For a moment I forgot where I was and absorbed the great silence and the deep calm with all my senses. I seemed for the first time to realize that the war was really over. At any rate the big war!

I heard someone clattering bowls and spoons and turned around. The country lad had left the apartment and had returned with my supper. I threw myself at the bowls even before his large hands had set them in their place, drank the soup noisily without worrying about the Russians' impression of my table manners and emptied another dish of potatoes, smoked pork and onions. Afterwards I felt a bit embarrassed. I stole a glance at the bedroom. The two Russians were sitting on the double bed munching their bread and regarding me with contented faces.

I wiped my mouth half ashamedly. The country lad had left a small packet of ten Papyrossi beside my plate—Russian cigarettes with a cardboard mouthpiece and a mixture of Turkish and Macedonian tobacco. Here was a chance of preserving the remnants of my dignity without personal sacrifice. I threw the packet through the open door onto the double bed. The Russians' eyes brightened. The small guy with the monkey face slipped the packet into his pocket.

"Don't you like them?" I asked.

"This better," answered the little guy. He pulled a paper from his tunic pocket and showed me the contents. I shuddered inwardly. It was my old friend the Mahorka. "We swap for this," he continued with a happy grin.

"Papyrossi too mild," said the country lad. "Papyrossi for officers, Mahorka for real soldiers!"

For a moment they looked at each other in amazement at their daring, as if they hadn't heard right. Then they doubled up on the bed and started shaking with laughter.

Later in the evening the colonel came up.

"Anything you need?" he asked in German and walked over to the window. He looked searchingly down on all sides.

"Only a bottle of Vodka, sir," I answered.

I thought I heard a faint snigger from the bedroom.

The colonel made a deprecating gesture. "No Vodka is issued on the active sectors of the front," he said in his monotonous, dry and slightly patronizing voice. "And we still regard Berlin as an active sector of the front."

"Then I suppose the victory paraders in the forest this morning were in one of the more quiet sectors of the Berlin front?" I ventured, using humor in an effort to pierce this cold unapproachable husk of a man.

"If you have observed the effects of alcohol in any of our troops, it will have been liquor they have obtained by their own efforts. This is strictly against the rules, but in view of the Red Army's great victory we do, in this transitional state, allow certain dispensations from some regulations."

He looked askance at me with his cold fish eyes as if he were peering over invisible glasses. It was the look of a military bureaucrat, containing both reproach for the drunken celebrators and annoyance at me because I interfered with matters that were none of my concern. Obviously humor was not the right approach.

"Will you please furnish me with all your particulars," he went on stiffly. "As exhaustive as possible. It is in your own interest."

He sat down, pulled out a large sheet of paper, which he had already divided into several columns, and started to cross question me methodically, writing down my answers. Most of his questions were intelligent and fair. Now and then when he would ask me something which I didn't think I had to answer, I just shook my head, whereupon he continued without further comment. I gave him a brief, but for the most part correct version of my activities in Berlin, naturally without mentioning any names or addresses. I supplied him with my O.S.S. number as I had arranged to do with my boss, so that my identity might be quickly established when I came out in the open after the capitulation. I also gave him my real name. It didn't mean anything now, but it might help to get my case quickly under way.

The interrogation lasted about an hour. Finally the colonel got up and pushed the papers in his pocket. Automatically his fingers searched for the center button of his uniform coat. His face took on a look of resignation, when he found as usual that he had to give up the idea of getting it buttoned across his stomach.

"Your information will now be subjected to close inquiries,"

236

he said with his hand on the doorknob. "But you have no need to worry. If you have told the truth, you will come to no harm, and you will be free to return to your own lines. In the Red Army you can always be sure of fair treatment."

I thought I heard a faint emphasis on the words "Red Army," and it was as if I saw for the first time a glimpse not so much of human as professional understanding in his cold fish eyes.

The following day during our morning ablutions which took place in the kitchen under a deluge of water but without soap, I exchanged formal introductions with the two Russian sentries. At first we were severely handicapped by language, because I found it very difficult to catch on to their army slang, but after a while it became easier as we learned to back up the spoken word with descriptive gestures and expressive mimicry.

The sentries both came from South Russia; the more exact geographical location was lost for all three of us in the vastness of the Russian domain. The little dark guy with the nutcracker face was called something like Kotja and the tall fair one seemed to go under the name of Abrasof. I could think of no good reason for wasting time on these tongue twisters.

"If you don't mind, I'll call you Abbott and Costello to make it easier," I told them, while I bent over the sink and let the cold water splash down on my naked body. It was good to feel the dirt disappear and the skin start to breathe again.

"Abbott and Costello are some good friends of mine in America. We often go to the movies together. What do you say? You're Costello," I said raising my head from the sink and nodding at the little dark guy. "And you're Abbott!" I pointed a wet finger at the country lad.

They repeated the names a couple of times, reflectively as if tasting them. Then they nodded brightly. It was okay with them.

My name caused them great difficulty. It seemed that their

237

tongues were not made for such sounds. All three of us thought hard.

"Amerikansky!" Costello finally cried, proud and relieved, as if he had just solved an exacting problem. And so it remained.

Amerikansky, Abbott and Costello settled down to a regular, daily routine.

I slept on the sofa while Abbott and Costello took turns at sleeping in the double bed, so that there was always one sentry awake during all of the twenty-four hours of the day. I slept like a log thanks to my Decodid tablets, which I had long before removed from my medicine chest and was carrying in my pocket. This seemed to impress the Russians, who found it hard to fall asleep. When I asked Costello why he couldn't sleep, his face twitched nervously. "Stalingrad," he said.

When I awoke, Abbott would fetch my tea in a large glass —half tea and half sugar until I took over mixing my own. Sometimes a friendly anonymous hand had put some jam in the tea before I got it.

At noon my lunch arrived, always boiled wheat grains with different kinds of meat. Then there was a quite superfluous afternoon tea. A couple of hours later a large, solid evening meal that consisted of much the same ingredients as lunch but always in a new variety and twice the amount. But I never got any fish, and there were days when I would have swapped all my overbrimming bowls of meat and potatoes for just one of Evald's wretched "whores." Finally at nine P.M., as the exhausting finish to the culinary race of the day, evening tea was served with cookies.

One evening as I pushed my plate away, full up and heavy as usual, though I had left a fair-sized portion of macaroni and meat, I happened to look into the bedroom, where Abbott and Costello occupied their customary positions at each end of the bed. For once they were not looking at me, but at my half-empty plate. It suddenly struck me that I hadn't seen them eat that day.

"Haven't you had anything?" I asked.

They shook their heads.

"But aren't you hungry?"

They nodded eagerly.

I pushed the chair back and got up to bring them what I had left. Abbott warded me off with outstretched hands.

# chapter thirteen

Every second of the day I thought of escaping, but as devoted as Abbott and Costello were while I observed the daily routine, just so suspicious were they at the slightest unusual gesture. They never left my side. They were extremely sensitive, registering like two barometers, one long the other short, the slightest change in my disposition.

One morning they both tactfully remained in the bedroom, anxious eyes following me as I walked up and down the room. I stopped in front of the open window. The large gray building surrounded by the high wall caught my eye. I knew by then that it was a school, and I could look down into the gymnasium with its parallel bars.

I leaned out of the window inquisitively. Something was going on over there. Two armed Russian sentries were posted at the entrance to the school grounds. In the gym two rows of men were lined up against the walls. The gym windows, placed a few feet above the ground, were open and even at a distance I could see how dingy the men looked. The two gray files moved slowly forward. Now and then a Russian soldier dragged one of the men out of the line, and they both disappeared somewhere farther up the gym. I was losing interest in the event—probably some Russian sorting out of the captured human material.

Then suddenly one of the Germans swung his legs over the sill of one of the windows facing me. As he landed on ground below, he started running along the concrete strip beside the building. I was moved by the sporting excitement a tourist experiences, watching two foreign teams at play, until I realized that the German didn't stand a chance. He made straight for the high wall surrounding the school yard. When he was just about to collide with it, he turned sharply about and like a cornered rat started scurrying along a short connecting wall to the right. I moved my eyes to the Russian sentries. They had spotted the German and were following his foolish, hopeless dash for freedom with obvious amusement. When finally the German, realizing that he was walled in, stopped in helpless confusion, one of the sentries casually raised his machine gun and gave him a short burst. The German took a few nimble dancing steps and folded up as if he had a hinge under his ribs. The sentry resumed his conversation with his comrade as if nothing had happened. I stepped back from the window. No, there was no possible way of escaping.

I sauntered over to the little bookcase. It contained a few German ladies' novels bound in cheap matching covers, the fruits of an energetic salesman's persuasive powers on a little German Hausmutter, who must have walked here dusting the bookcase. I browsed around in one of the books and put it back again. . . .

I could not keep myself from returning to the window. The German was still lying down there on the concrete strip. The lawn beside the white concrete shone with a deep green in the sun. The Russian sentries chatted and laughed. I felt the spring in my blood. I took a deep breath and went over to lie on the sofa, staring up at the ceiling. All the world was liberated except me—

and the guy lying over there on the concrete. But maybe he had been liberated in a way. I hardly noticed when one of my Russian guards left the apartment.

An hour went by, and then I heard a loud racket outside the door, as if someone had dropped a lot of small heavy objects. Costello opened the door. Standing outside was Abbott, his arms full of books.

"There you are, Amerikansky!" he said with a joyous expression in his blue eyes. He moved carefully to the table and placed the books on it.

"Where on earth did you get those?" I asked in surprise and got up from the sofa.

Abbott made a wide sweeping gesture, that included the entire apartment house.

The two Russians lifted the table and moved the display of books over to the window. I started to pick out some volumes, curious to find out about the average literary tastes of a working-class German. The Russians pushed me gently but firmly aside. That was one of the traces of communism I observed in them: all reading matter was in principle an evil, unless it had been passed by censor.

Their system was simple but efficient. They judged the books by their covers.

A handsome copy of *Mein Kampf*, which the former owner probably had not had time to destroy, went out through the open window, followed by an equally rare copy of Goebbels's *Vom Kaiserhof zur Reichskanzlei*. The dull thuds on the pavement downstairs suggested executions in effigy of the respective authors. I had no objections. Three or four volumes of earlier vintage were hastily looked through and approved. A large pile of pamphlets on the nazistic workers' front were sent to join Messrs. Hitler and Goebbels. In the end there were only eight books left, and these Costello handed me with motherly affection. They made up my spiritual nourishment during the rest of the time I stayed at the apartment. Most of them were about the former German East-African colonies. I read them all.

One of the books was a major work on the Franco-Prussian war of 1870-71. It contained some handsome full-page engravings on fine glazed paper, the other side of which had been left blank. This was to come in very handy in other ways.

But the gem of the collection was a stack of old programmes from the 1936 Olympic Games in Berlin. Abbott and Costello looked through them carefully, giving special attention to some delicious full-page photographs in which the American swimming girls were displaying their long, slender limbs. When they had finished their scrutiny, I tore out the photographs and stuck them in a fan of pin-ups on the wall above the sofa.

We all stepped a few paces back to study the effect.

"Do you like them?" I asked.

For a long time they thought furiously to find an answer that did not fall too short of the truth and at the same time would not hurt my national pride.

"Well, they're not so bad," Abbott said.

"But rather thin," Costello added.

Two more days passed, during which new inhabitants of the apartment below began to get on my nerves. Judging by the row they kicked up all day and night they would be Russian soldiers posted to the most quiet section of the Berlin front, where the restrictions on vodka or privately provided liquor were nonexistent. The door to their apartment was always half open, and when I went down to the lavatory there would be a Russian framed in the doorway gaping at me.

But my worst enemy during these days was still boredom. Once again I felt the icy breath of the fog: of being totally forgotten and buried alive. In these pessimistic moments I thought of how many Russians there were in this world, how many there might be in the next when you subtracted the party members, and by using simple arithmetic I realized that there was no reason at all for anyone in this great reservoir of human beings to worry about one life more or less.

The colonel had not showed up again, nor had the captain, although in my restlessness I would almost have welcomed their company. Finally I felt I had to do something. I asked for a pencil, and with grave misgivings Costello lent me one. On the reverse side of an engraving from *The Franco-Prussian War*, showing a spike-helmeted Bismarck, soldier of the old school, and probably one of the colonel's secret idols, I composed a long letter pointing out in a polite but firm manner that it was a breach of international law to hold back an ally as prisoner of war, especially as the war was over. I signed it with my O.S.S. number in case the colonel had forgotten it.

I went in to Costello and made him swear a solemn oath that he would personally deliver the letter to the colonel. Abbott had gone to fetch the tea. Costello was standing by the double bed. His hand caressed one of the big brass knobs fixed on each of the four bedposts.

"Gold?" he asked, as if he had made a profitable discovery.

I laughed. "No, Costello, only a cheap metal! Very ordinary bed."

The information came as a shock to him, but he was not convinced. "Gold! Capitalist!" he asserted, looking around the room.

I tried to tell him that most people in Western Europe lived that way, at any rate they had before the war. He looked at me reproachfully and disappointed, as if he had just caught an old friend trying to pull a fast one on him. To him and his pal this apartment, with its cheap taste and lack of anything of value, was the height of luxury. Neither of them had ever been so comfortable as they were here, and they couldn't understand why I was so anxious to get home. Home to them was any place where they had a reasonably good time.

They were quite touching in their eager efforts to brighten up my existence. From one of his many bundles Costello brought out a chessboard with ivory pieces which he had probably stolen somewhere or other. He played brilliantly, sweeping my pawns, officers and royalty in quick succession off the board. Like most other normal people I didn't like losing and besides I didn't think I could afford to lose face before Costello's triumphant grin. I suggested that we play halma instead, a far less difficult game that I remembered from my childhood. I played safe by giving Costello a very poor explanation of the rules beforehand and by playing the game with terrific speed. The halma went to America and the balance was restored.

Next day, when my spirits had fallen below zero because the colonel had not replied to my letter, Costello disappeared and stayed away for a long time. Abbott was busy with an old radio and loud-speaker which they had brought up to the apartment, where I had got it going. The urge to experiment was itching in Abbott's as in all Russian fingers. He labored happily with the vital parts of the instrument. Suddenly there was a bang and a *pfuif*, as if a flash of lightning had zigzagged through the loud-speaker. Abbott stood there with the cable in his hand, looking lost.

"You've connected up the loud-speaker directly with the switch, you oaf," I said resignedly. "It's finished now! Bust!"

Abbott didn't say a word. He tiptoed round the room and stopped in front of the piano. Suddenly he brought one large fist crashing down on the keys. He grabbed the loud-speaker and flung it through the window. Involuntarily I ducked my head. He was a powerful guy with a great deal of latent strength, but a moment later he was his inoffensive, quiet self again. The loud-speaker had disappeared not only out of the window but also out of his mind forever.

At long last Costello returned. I could see by his face that something unusual had happened. He carried a parcel wrapped in dirty newspaper. He lifted a corner of the wrapping and looked at me with an expression of playful secrecy, as if he would say, "Now you are going to get the biggest surprise of your life!"

He put the parcel on the floor and started to undo it. Inside was a toy train, a cheap, German toy train with a small clockwork engine and some tin rails with a track switch.

"Engineer!" cried Costello proudly, straddling his legs as he watched the little locomotive wobbling over its short circular route. I looked at him without understanding until I suddenly realized that he thought he had acquired a rare and valuable engineer's scale model.

I couldn't very well refrain from joining in the game. We all sat down on the floor. I as the competent, mild but firm director of the railroad, Abbott and Costello taking turns as eager but rather clumsy drivers and switchmen. The afternoon passed, the blackest afternoon in the history of railroading, packed with catastrophes and derailments, until the locomotive seemed to buzz round inside my head, and I had to go and lie down on the sofa.

Without technical supervision Abbott and Costello very quickly wrecked the switch system and blocked the rails. Far from being upset, they just swept the track aside and sat down facing each other with their backs to the opposing walls of the room, letting the little train run backwards and forwards over the floor between them. The two happy railway magnates were still at it when I finally fell asleep.

I had spent about ten days in the apartment, when the colonel finally showed up. Gravely he laid his hat on the table. I looked at him expectantly. He cleared his throat, peered at me over imaginary family-physician glasses and said, "I have received your letter which I have studied very closely. Presuming that you are the person you claim to be, I must admit that on the whole I share your views."

I thought I heard just a slight intonation in his voice that told me my literary efforts had not been quite in vain.

"Unfortunately," he continued, "you have aroused the suspicion of others who also have a say in this matter. And I cannot say I blame them. Are you quite sure you cannot give us something that will establish your identity beyond all doubt? Your contact among the Americans or some such information?"

"I have told you all that you can reasonably demand of me as an officer," I answered firmly. "Would you have done more, if you had landed up behind the American lines?"

He ignored the question and picked up his hat. "Your case will be expedited as much as possible," he said and turned to go. "Is there anything you need?"

He let his eyes wander round the room and stopped at the pin-up fan over the sofa. His lips tightened in a thin, bloodless smile and he shook his head almost imperceptibly at a human folly which he himself had long since overcome. Then the door closed behind him.

There was a sound of sniggering from the bedroom. Even if Abbott and Costello hadn't understood a word of the conversation which was carried on in the colonel's broken German, they had seen a lot in the colonel's expression as he left the room, and they were now turning it over in their enterprising minds.

For the next hour or so there was a constant whispering from the double bed. The two Russians had nothing else to do. It was one of their days of fasting, but that evening they went as far as to accept the sugar I had not used in my tea. For some unknown reason there seemed to be a tense and almost expectant atmosphere in the apartment. It was like the eve of a big and decisive battle. Abbott and Costello couldn't settle down in their own room, but crept around in the apartment with an ambiguous expression, as if they were guarding a dark secret which they could hardly forbear to tell.

Eventually they had to find release for their suppressed excitement. Abbott sat down at the piano. He had developed sufficient skill to back up his little one finger tunes with quite harmonious balalaika-like chords. He sang the words of the tune in a clear deep baritone. Some days before Costello had discovered that he could lift up the lid of the piano, and he stared in fascination at all the little hammers tapping on the wires.

Neither of them had ever seen a piano before. The new discovery had developed Abbott's inherited ear for music and Costello's talents as a mechanic. Once more it struck me that these Russians were like children who each day found something new to challenge their ability and quickness of mind. They were clumsy and unsure of themselves at first; when they suddenly faced something new, they were timorous and jumpy like wild animals afraid of a trap, but when they had held some new thing in their hands just once, felt it, shaken it and better still taken it apart, they were amazingly quick at grasping its technical composition.

When I awoke the next morning, Abbott had disappeared. He came back around noon and, with a sour and disappointed expression, laid the table for lunch. Then Costello disappeared. I could hardly bear the sight of food any more. Weary and overfed I pushed the plate as far across the table as possible, took one of the books from my library and lay down on the sofa.

I started to re-read a chapter on German railroad building in East Africa, although I already knew the name of every station on its goddam fever-infested track, every platform and every sleeper. I read on dully, without the slightest interest, as if I were studying for some completely irrelevant exam which I could forget as quickly as I liked afterwards. Abbott found it very difficult to keep still. He kept looking impatiently towards the door, but I couldn't even be bothered to take any interest in what might be bothering him. I was fed up with East African trains, with toy trains on tin rails, with halma, chess, boiled wheat grains, with the eternal spring sun and the stinking toilets, with the noise from the apartment below. I was fed to the teeth with the whole setup.

There was a sound of footsteps from the stairway, dragging steps, as if someone was carrying a heavy load up the stairs. It must be an exceptionally awkward and heavy burden, because now and then the man stopped, set his load down with a bump and took a rest to gather strength for the next flight. I supposed that one of the Russian soldiers living down below had been abroad collecting stores. But the dragging steps and the bumps continued past their apartment and up to ours.

When the man and his burden had reached my door, there were strange sounds of a struggle. I signaled Abbott to see what it could be. He only laughed knowingly and stared at the door which at the same time flew open. A girl staggered a few steps into the room and stopped, leaning backwards, stiff as a board, against Costello's hand that held her neck in a tight grip. Costello shoved her a bit further into the apartment. Then he put his free hand in his trouser pocket, fetched out a key, locked the door, and put the key back in his pocket. Not till then did he let go of the girl who, without altering her rigid, unnatural attitude, fell backwards against the door. There she remained standing.

Costello wiped the sweat off his brow and flashed me a triumphant grin. He opened his mouth to say something, but apparently concluded that words might spoil the general effect. Instead he pointed with an unmistakable gesture at the sofa and gave Abbott, who had been watching with an expression of intense happiness, a nudge with his elbow. Both men disappeared into the bedroom, significantly closing the door behind them.

The girl, still standing, had so flattened herself against the locked door that she almost appeared to be in bas-relief —work showing the utmost human fear and terror. Even behind her unflattering spectacles, I could see that her eyes were glazed in panic.

I was reminded of those cartoons that show the unceremonious and hard-handed way the stone-age man treats his women. I laughed out loud, something I hadn't done since the day Abbott burned his fingers on the piano.

My laughter, which the girl naturally mistook for the lecherous grin from a scruffy, bearded monster, nearly sent her through the closed door.

"I presume you are German?" I asked, speaking in that language.

Not a muscle moved in the girl's frozen face. Her distended fingers looked as if they were glued to the door.

With my hands shoved casually into my pockets, I walked over to the window to give her time to recover. Half annoyed, I caught myself looking at that dark spot on the concrete where the German had folded up.

After a while I turned and looked at her. Her fingers were shaking, and there was a flicker in her eyes as I moved towards her.

Panic-stricken, she burst out hysterically, "Not now! Can't it—can't it wait?" She tore her hands from the door and stretched them in front of her defensively.

"I'm not Russian," I said curtly, and pulled a chair from the dining table. "Sit down a moment and relax. No one here will do you any harm."

She didn't move.

"Didn't you hear me?" I said, annoyed. "Sit down!"

She crept slowly forward and perched on the edge of the chair. Her skirt was very short and had probably shrunk after countless washings and ironings. Nervously she pulled it down over her knees, but a moment later it had crept up again. I decided that she probably had very nice legs under the ugly woollen stockings she wore.

"What's your name?" I asked, and sat down at the table facing her. She did not answer.

"Surely you've got a name?" I shouted impatiently.

"Hilde," she whispered barely audibly. Her skin was young and smooth. She was probably in her late twenties.

"Now listen, Hilde," I said, leaning across the table. "I'm an American officer. All this is just a misunderstanding. One of my guards took it in his own head to bring you up here. You are free to leave whenever you wish."

I started towards the bedroom door, behind which I could sense a deep and expectant silence, to ask Costello for the key of the door. Then suddenly I got an idea.

"By the way, aren't you hungry?" I asked. I went back to the table and pushed my half empty plate towards her. "Go on, don't be shy. You just eat it up!"

For a brief moment she hovered between fear and hunger. Then she threw caution to the winds and bent over the plate, shovelling in the food.

Her hair hung in long strands over her forehead and almost touched the food. There was no trace of make-up on her face. Her dress sagged over her shoulders and breast completely hiding the contours of her body. But it seemed to me that her hair was too disordered to be natural. Those loose strands had the appearance of a hairstyle in themselves, a clever attempt to create an impression of plain homeliness. Hungry as she was, she still handled her knife and fork correctly, and though her hands were dirty, she had not been able to disguise the long slender wrists or the slim supple fingers.

I pushed my glass of tea, which I hadn't touched, over to her. She regarded it doubtfully.

"You may not be able to see that it is tea," I said, smiling. "Wouldn't it improve your eyesight if you took off those glasses?"

She blushed—most becomingly.

The usual packet of Papyrossi was lying on the table. I offered her one and lit it for her.

"Go on, take those glasses off and let me see what you really look like," I said cheerfully. "Maybe I will appear less terrifying to you, if you do."

She removed the glasses, hesitatingly, as if she were taking off her last intimate piece of clothing to face me naked.

"Well, well! That's quite different," I said with conviction. All at once she had become ten years younger.

She had brown eyes, wide awake and intelligent now that they were no longer covered with the gray film of terror. She flashed me an embarrassed smile. "I'm so afraid of. . . ."

She didn't finish the sentence. Deep down in her brown eyes uncertainty still lurked. She looked at me searchingly as if she was not yet completely sure of my intentions.

"I understand what you mean," I said. "At the beginning of May I saw a bit of everything in the west of the town."

"Here in Berlin?" she asked puzzled.

"As I told you before, I am an American officer. I am waiting to be transferred to my own lines. I was interned by the Russians in Berlin."

"Do you think the Americans will be here soon?" she asked eagerly. Then, with an unconscious attempt at coquetry, "Are all Americans like you?"

"Sure they're coming—and they're all a lot more handsome than I," I said, rubbing a hand over my bristly beard.

"And will I have to. . . . ? She looked down at the glasses she had laid beside the empty plate.

"No, you won't have to."

There was a pause. She sipped the tea neatly, well mannered as a lady.

"I suppose you have been through it all?" I finally asked. I let my hand describe a steeply climbing movement and then let it flop down beside the chair again. She understood the gesture.

"Yes, I've been through it all," she said in a hard voice, as if it gave her courage not to deny it.

The cigarette ash fell down in the tea glass with a small hissing sound. Hilde gave a start, and when she turned her eyes towards me, I saw that they were filled with tears.

"Come now, Hilde," I said, "all that is over now." I could

253

hear myself how ridiculous it sounded. For her it had just started.

I got up and walked across and opened the bedroom door.

"Costello," I said with all the authority I could pack into my voice. "Take the German lady back where you found her. And no tricks!" I fixed him with a stern look.

Costello peered inquisitively at the sofa. Disappointment spread over his features. He looked at me quizzically. I shook my head. "Do as I say," I ordered.

As Hilde went out, she threw me a look through her glasses, which she had put back on. I couldn't read what was in it, for the glasses were blurred with tears.

# chapter fourteen

During the remainder of the day Abbott and Costello wandered around with a crestfallen look. They had tried to brighten up my existence. The capture of Hilde had been their master stroke. And when that hadn't helped, what was left to them to think of now? In their faces I could read wonder as to why I was so bad-tempered and difficult. Why didn't I ever think of anything but getting home? Didn't I have everything that any man could reasonably ask for? A roof over my head, plenty of food at regular intervals, nothing to do and a girl just around the corner if I could be bothered to reach my hand out.

I did my best to make them understand that, now the war was over, my time as a soldier was up. At home I had a job and a family waiting for me. They shook their heads. I realized that they did not regard their military service as a parenthetic, temporary period of their lives that would be over someday. They had already been in the Red Army for six years and many of their companions had been in considerably longer. The army had come to be their home, the rank and file their family, and the eternal marching the purpose of their existence. They no longer knew any civilian trade. War was their job now, they understood it, and it crowded their lives with events, no matter where or against whom it was carried out.

"But surely you have a family?" I asked.

They looked at each other. The word struck no note of recognition in either of them. Yes—somewhere or other, in that vast place called Russia, there might be someone who knew them by name.

And what if the family had moved to some other spot? Well, they guessed they would find it sometime, somehow. That was all something that had to wait until the day when they would be demobilized, a faraway, misty prospect, lost somewhere way out in the future which they never gave a thought, anyway. On that improbable day they would be detrained at some chance station, from which, with the aid of the Russians' almost infallible homing-pigeon instinct, they would start the long trek back to the village they had once left to join up. They had no doubt that they would find it, and everything would be the same as in the old days. Just as the distances in that country are far greater than anywhere else, time also has its own special Russian dimensions. Five years, ten years—they are just a whisper of the winds across the steppes.

Abbott and Costello were soldiers of a type that is new in modern Europe, but old in history. The mercenary, whose brother is the man beside him and whose father is the colonel. They never longed for civilian life, either because they had never known it, or else because they had forgotten it. That is the main difference between the Russian soldier and a soldier in the armies of the democracies. British and American soldiers, no matter how strongly they feel their patriotic duty, will always be split personalities, divided between the world they have been torn away from—homes, parents, wives and sweethearts, jobs—and the world they have suddenly been thrown into. They will never accept the army as their primary existence but on the contrary try to adapt their army life to those customs and to that mentality they have brought with them from their homes.

Abbott and Costello were not split between two worlds. They were whole people. Their military service was not a job limited to this location, that year or any particular war. Their life was the army and in that life days like those spent in the apartment formed a wonderful interlude. For that reason they could not understand my attitude.

It was a bit easier for me to understand them. From time to time I saw them in my mind's eye—not as the gentle, spring-happy Abbott and Costello of their apartment Eldorado, but as mercenaries once more on the march. The thought filled me with uneasiness.

Meanwhile, I kept the colonel informed about the developments of the 1870-71 Franco-Prussian war. One engraving after the other was despatched, the reverse side covered with protests, arguments and appeals to him personally as well as to the Red Army. I got steadily more restless and nervous. I wrote in a state of panic just to give him a daily reminder of my existence, so that I should not be entirely forgotten.

The mysterious inhabitants of the apartment below had started to pay us visits. They were big, rough types like the men I had seen on guard in front of the captain's office on the day I went to be questioned. They crossed the sitting room glowering at me on the sofa and disappeared into the bedroom. As a rule they had bottles with them. The bedroom door was pulled to but not completely closed, and while the bottles went round, the guests and my two guards conversed at length in low whispers. Abbott and Costello were usually a bit unsteady on their legs after the visitors had left, but that was the only change I noticed in their attitude towards me.

One morning, when Abbott had been on his customary daily mail-run to the colonel, he came back to the apartment with a small ladies' wrist watch carefully concealed in his huge fist. It ticked very irregularly like the heart in the breast of some terrified bird, and finally it stopped completely. Abbott mourned it deeply, and when he had finished his duties for that day he filed the point of his penknife to a slim watch-maker's tool, snapped the back off the watch and carefully began to remove the works. He put all the little pieces in neat separate piles on the tablecloth after a set pattern. I lay on my sofa watching him, completely absorbed in his delicate task.

Finally I fell asleep, but around eleven P.M. I was wakened by a terrible row. One of the biggest and most repulsive of the soldiers downstairs came thundering into our apartment. He was drunk and in a thick voice he started a typical inebriate conversation with Abbott who was still bending over his intricate work. Abbott answered him only in words of one syllable, which seemed to annoy the visitor, who became belligerent. Abbott raised his head and told him in a firm voice to get out. The drunken Russian grinned sheepishly, staggered over to the table and bent over it, as if he really wanted to admire Abbott's skill. Suddenly he raised his hand to sweep it across the tablecloth, but drunk as he was, the movement misfired, and he reeled like a groggy prize fighter. In a flash Abbott was on his feet, whipping his fist into the other man's face and sending him staggering back against the wall. Abbott quickly followed up, grabbed him by the neck, opened the door and kicked him down the stairs. Then he locked the door carefully and returned to his work. It was the first time during my stay in the apartment that the door had been locked at night, and it was the first time in a week that I slept really soundly.

I woke up because Abbott was standing by the sofa and shaking my arm. The morning sun fell directly on his blue eyes that shone as if they had been polished.

"Barin!" he cried triumphantly. "It is going!" He held the watch to my ear, and sure enough the little heart was ticking away again, somewhat irregularly but still ticking.

I didn't know what to be most surprised about—that he had made the watch go in the course of the night, or that in his excitement he had used the old Russian word for Lord, Barin—a word that had been banned by the Communists since 1920.

Later that morning the captain appeared. There was no ingratiating smile and no questions as to my welfare. The mask he wore was that of the cold investigator giving an obdurate sinner his last chance to come clean.

"Well, have you thought of something that might speed up your case? Some useful little piece of information that will lighten our task in placing you?" he asked.

I shook my head. "In my letters to the colonel——"

"The colonel!" he interrupted. "It's not the colonel you are dealing with now. It's me asking you. You can go on writing to the colonel till your fingers warp, it still won't do you any good unless you co-operate with me. Have you nothing further to say?" he demanded, his voice quivering with suppressed fury.

Again I shook my head.

He walked right up to me and poked a finger into my face. "May I remind you of a few things," he said, his anger changing to vicious sarcasm. "You were sent to Berlin for some unknown purpose at a time, when it had already been decided that Berlin should be occupied by the Russians. What business has an American agent in a city that already in effect belongs to us?"

He looked at me triumphantly, as if he had just slashed away the curtain that hid my secret.

"In my instructions it was not predicted that the Russians would enter Berlin alone," I replied. "I know nothing about the decision you speak of."

He brushed aside my argument. "You have tried to tell us a lot about your task in Berlin, but you have forgotten to tell us the most important part. You were not the last secret agent against the Germans; you were the first secret agent—against us!"

He made a dramatic pause so that the implication of his words could really sink deep down into my mind. I felt ill at ease because his words far from sinking down soared higher and higher, reaching the airy clouds of lunacy where everything is possible.

"Why, then, would I give myself up voluntarily?" I asked, keeping up the illusion that it had been voluntarily.

"Because your task was completed, and you had the audacity to try to make use of our transport to get home. Your successors are probably already on their way."

I shrugged my shoulders. He looked at me for a moment, hatefully—and probably for once sincerely—opened his mouth to say something, thought better of it, and left the room, slamming the door behind him.

That night it happened. Costello had taken the precaution to lock the door as on the previous night. I had had some doubts as to the inward sympathies of my guards, but now I realized that I probably should never have doubted that to them an order was an order—and the supreme law of their existence. The colonel's order that they should guarantee my safety had probably been sufficient in itself, but the episode with the watch had made the whole matter their personal problem too.

None of us slept. The row from the downstairs apartment was more violent than ever before. There was shouting and tinkling of bottles. I tossed and turned on the sofa. It was as if the fumes of alcohol seeped through the floor from below and filled my room with a thick atmosphere that gave me a headache. I heard footsteps on the stairs, and somebody went into the apartment downstairs. Instantly the noise ceased. I crept from the sofa and put my ear against the floor. The only sound that drifted up was a low voice speaking curtly as if giving orders. Something in the tense atmosphere told me that a decisive move was imminent. The noctural visitor left the downstairs apartment again. Costello, who was on duty and sitting at the table, suddenly straightened up listening. He summoned his comrade in a whisper. Abbott answered with a grunt that told us he was also wide awake.

For a long time we sat listening. The silence downstairs was conspicuous. Now and then I thought I could hear muffled metallic sounds. Costello took a quick look around the room, waved Abbott over to him and whispered a few words in his ear. Abbott hurried into the bedroom and came out carrying two machine guns. There were creeping footsteps on the stairs. With a curt gesture Costello motioned me into the bedroom. I was about to protest, when Abbott gripped me by the arm and pushed me in there without further ado.

Suddenly the door handle was wrenched around from the outside as if someone wanted to make sure that his entry would be a startling surprise. When the man discovered that the door was locked, there was a quick whispered conference outside on the landing. There were at least three men out there.

Costello took cover behind a projection in the wall. Abbott crouched down behind his beloved piano. Both had their machine guns at the ready position.

"Open up, you idiots!" said a voice from outside. "We've come to fetch the American. Captain's orders!"

Costello answered, raising his machine gun, "Don't know anything about that. We only let go of the American on the colonel's orders! Why don't you go fetch the colonel?"

He was interrupted by a burst of machine-gun fire through the door. Small wooden splinters flew all over the room. Some of the bullets ended up with little plonking thuds in the wall above the sofa, but most of them struck where they supposedly were meant to strike—right in the sofa itself.

My two guards reacted in a flash. They were no longer Abbott and Costello, but two Russian soldiers whose job was war—any time, any place and against anyone. Without even looking at each other, but like two artists who have been working together a long time and know the routine, they fired simultaneously from their respective corners, sending a long burst through the door. The bullets ripped two jagged streaks in the door two feet above the floor. There was a roar from the landing and the sound of a heavy body falling. At the same time there was a haphazard burst of fire through the door from the outside, but it seemed to be coming from someone whose legs were knocked away beneath him as he pressed the trigger. A few stray bullets whacked into the piano, making the wires clang. I heard a muffled curse from Abbott. Outside a brief violent argument started. Someone was being supported down the stairs. The street door was slammed, and a profound silence settled over the battlefield.

My two guards remained in their positions for a while with their machine guns pointing at the door and their fingers on the triggers. Finally Costello got up, crept carefully over to the door, turned the key with a swift movement and flung the door open. He looked quickly to both sides, closed the door again and locked it. Abbott came out from behind the piano and went over to the sofa. He was limping. He sat down on top of the plaster that had crumbled down from the wall, where the bullets struck home.

I walked over to him. "Anything serious, Abbott?" I asked.

Costello helped him get his boot off and rolled up his long underpants. There was blood on one leg of his pants. Costello regarded the leg professionally. Then he looked up at me and proudly said, "Russian boots okay, huh?"

They certainly were. They had taken the main impact of the bullet.

The next morning the colonel appeared in the kitchen door. He was breathing heavily, as if he had taken the stairs in one leap. At the same time he seemed to be very angry and I could see that Abbott and Costello had got the same impression, for the two soldiers, who were not usually very ceremonious, jumped smartly to attention.

"You cannot stay here any longer," he exclaimed, speaking to me. "You are undermining the morale of our soldiers. You are the cause of dissension here in the compound. I can no longer take the responsibility of keeping you here. You have become a problem, which can only be solved in one way: You must disappear!" I started violently. "You must try to contact the Americans yourself!"

The noose around my neck was raised and disappeared overhead once more. Those were the most encouraging words I had heard from the mouth of any Russian. These strange, unpredictable people whose next move you could never foretell. I just couldn't understand this colonel who was standing before me and virtually letting me go.

I bowed my head in shame because I hadn't been able to help him in his difficulties.

"I am sorry to have caused you so much trouble, Colonel. But as an American officer—"

He interrupted me with a weary gesture, while his face puckered up in a grimace that showed his revulsion for this well-worn sentence, which he had heard and read until he knew it in his sleep. I felt a small pang of disappointment because he wouldn't listen to all the beautifully polished arguments I had spent the whole previous afternoon printing neatly on the reverse side of the last of the engravings from *The Franco-Prussian War*. It showed Napoleon the Third, deep in dismal thoughts after being captured at Sedan. For my part I felt that the nameless artist's portrayal of the unhappy scene could not fail to make a lasting impression on the hardest of Russian hearts.

The colonel opened the door and pointed at two soldiers who were waiting outside on the landing.

"These men will escort you to Magdeburg, where the Russo-American exchange of prisoners of war, interned and deported persons is taking place. Maybe they will be able to decide

263

there to which category you belong," he said with a malicious gleam in his eyes, as if he were already enjoying the discomfort of his colleagues trying to find the right shelf for me.

"When do I leave?" I asked.

"Right away," he replied impatiently. "Pack your things and clear out of the apartment in ten minutes."

He made a reluctant movement with his hand towards the peak of his cap. Right to the very end he was in doubt of where to place me. I rated two fifths of a salute.

When he had left, I hurried into the kitchen, and in a cupboard I found a small, battered fiber case which the Russians had not deigned to steal. Luggage, no matter how humble and insignificant, will always make a man appear more trustworthy. A moment later I was back in the room looking around for something to put in the suitcase. Costello caught on and grabbed the first thing he could see. It turned out to be *The Franco-Prussian War*, lying on the table.

I shook my head with a smile, but as I couldn't find anything better myself, I finally put it in the suitcase.

Then I grabbed my crumpled hat and said good-bye to Abbott and Costello. They shook my hand with a sad but at the same time rather vacant look which told me that I was already on my way out of their minds, and that their sorrow was caused less by my departure than by the thought that their untroubled, idle life in the apartment was coming to an end.

From the doorway, I threw them a last, fond look. Then I let my eyes wander round the room where I had been sitting or lying for three weeks. The pin-ups over the sofa flashed me their sterile cheesecake smiles, and for the first time I noticed that one of them had been grievously wounded by one of the stray bullets during the nocturnal skirmish. I closed the door hurriedly.

My two new guards were waiting on the landing. One of them, a corporal, was armed with a machine gun. The other was, as far as I could see, a private. It was hard to get a view of him, because he was partly concealed under an enormous, bulging haversack. I increased the pace as we passed the apartment below, but there was no sound behind the closed door. When we reached the street, the corporal was undecided as to which barrier we should choose. I took the liberty of pointing out the one that in my opinion should open up on the road towards the southwest, and the corporal followed my suggestion.

We had a terrible time getting past the barrier. The corporal flashed a lot of papers, and the amazon in the sentry box covered them with an equal amount of stamps. My apprehensions that this should turn out to be a trap were gradually dispersed. If they had picked this blue spring morning to shoot me, why make such a complicated affair of it, when it would be just as easy to take me round the back of some ruined wall?

When the corporal and the amazon had been playing post office for a long time in the sentry box, they came out and started a furious argument, accompanied by wild gesticulations. The amazon pointed in one direction, whereupon the corporal beat his brow. Then the corporal pointed in another direction, and the amazon promptly imitated his dramatic gesture. The cause of their strife seemed to be something as unimportant as a small strange sound that started at the back of their throats and came rolling out gutturally over their tongues. They threw this little sound at each other so often that I finally realized it was the Russian version of Magdeburg. I pulled the corporal's sleeve gently and pointed towards the south. The corporal gave the amazon a triumphant look that said as much as, "See what I told you, numskull!"

The amazon crinkled her nose and turned to raise the barrier. There had been no need for her to give in so easily, for south was the only direction in which neither of them had pointed.

When we had been walking for about fifteen minutes and had long since lost sight of the barrier, I expressed my jubilation in a merry whistle. A man kept inside four walls, no matter under what conditions, will always be a prisoner. But a man on the march, even under escort, will feel that things have started moving, something's happening at last, that he is on his way to something new, which people always confuse with something better. This time, however, I did not feel the victim of false illusions. I really believed that I was on my way to freedom.

Half an hour went by, then we heard the sound of an engine. A truck of some American model, with a Russian driver at the wheel, was heading towards us.

The corporal stuck a hand in the air.

"Jump on," cried the driver, a young, handsome fellow in the uniform of a corporal. The private loaded himself and the sack onto the truck platform. My corporal and I squeezed in beside the driver who looked questioningly at us.

"We are going to Magdeburg," said my corporal, trying hard to give it my pronunciation with the accent on all syllables.

"We're going south," I explained.

The two corporals started a sniggering conversation which suggested that they too had served on one of the more quiet sectors of the Berlin front. There was no traffic on the road, and the driver let the truck have its own way.

When we had covered another seven or eight miles, the truck was no longer going our way, so we got out. My corporal looked wistfully after the truck and reluctantly struck out along the highway that stretched like an endless white ribbon to the horizon. The sun was scorching down on us. The corporal unbuttoned his tunic collar. The private puffed and groaned under his burden. The corporal's pace grew slower and slower. At last he stopped, looking in all directions, as if to conjure up some transport.

"Are we on the right road?" he asked. His voice told me

that he was a man strongly determined to avoid one single unnecessary step.

"Yes, we should be, according to the sun," I answered.

He squinted suspiciously at the glowing orb and looked miserably down the long, white strip. Any other road but this one, I read in his eyes. Then he resigned himself, hoisted up his machine gun and prepared to go on.

Supposing he gets so tired that he leaves me, I thought in alarm. He was carrying all my papers. Then I got an idea.

"Couldn't we take turns?" I asked and pointed to the machine gun. "My suitcase is much lighter."

The corporal grabbed the suitcase and tested it suspiciously. His face brightened. "Every other mile?" he suggested.

We plodded on, I carrying the machine gun and the corporal with the *Franco-Prussian War* in the suitcase. The scenery around us was so quiet and full of Sunday peace that we all found this exchange of roles quite natural. I was making for Berliner Ring, the autobahn that encircles Berlin, from which we could take the road for Magdeburg.

We finally reached the autobahn about sunset. The corporal woke from the apathy the last few hours of marching had sent him into and started looking along the sides of the road to find someplace where we could spend the night in the open air —the most natural thing for a Russian soldier. To my great relief we suddenly spied a log cabin, lying a little way off the autobahn. There was smoke coming out of the chimney.

My own feet were also a bit sore, so I sent my most fervent wishes with the corporal when he disappeared into the log cabin. A moment later he was standing in the doorway, waving us over. He was one big smile and all weariness seemed to have left him.

There was no light in the log cabin when I entered, but the glow from a fire on the hearth flickered over the tarred walls, giving the room a warm and friendly air. The corporal was bending over the fire beside a hefty but well-proportioned Russian girl, wearing the usual amazon uniform. She was not as short-legged nor as broad-bosomed as the barrier girls I had seen at the compound.

She raised her head, brushed her black hair from her forehead and sent me a look in which there seemed to be sparks from the fire. A wild, slightly tousled but curvaceous beauty. The corporal who stuck close to her had apparently come to the same conclusion.

The amazon shouldered her carbine in the same matter-of-fact way a man would hitch up his pants, and bade me welcome. The corporal explained that the log cabin was a former German guard hut, now used as a canteen for the Russian traffic on the autobahn. Our armed girl friend was canteen hostess.

They bent over the fire again, and I greedily sniffed the aroma of fried potatoes and smoked ham. Real food, instead of that synthetic stuff from the haversack.

We sat down at a long oak table each with a well-filled plate before him. Our hostess sat at the head of the table, still carrying the carbine over one shoulder.

"Don't you like my cooking?" she asked, when I finally pushed my partly emptied plate away and replete leaned back against the timber walls. I would not have been too surprised by an ominous rattle of the carbine, but I heard only the voice of a worried and rather disappointed housewife.

Shortly afterwards when we had cleared away the dishes, the carbine rattled in earnest from the darkest corner of the room, where the corporal had remained with our hostess, presumably to express in a thorough manner his gratitude for the meal. At the same time I heard her high-pitched, teasing laughter. The corporal came slinking back to us, long in the face.

"How can you get some light in this place?" he shouted to the hostess, who had walked over to the fireplace, where she stood doing up her tunic with an air of unconcern. Obviously annoyed he pulled a piece of paper and a pencil from one of his pockets. The private, who had emptied my plate as well as his own, belched loudly and followed the corporal's example.

The hostess went into the little kitchen situated in a small wing of the cabin, and returned with a bottle and a potato, which she placed on the table. Then she bent down and deftly pulled a thread from an old rug, lying on the bench behind the table. The flickering light from the fire threw her shadow onto the timber wall like a giant poster of a daughter of the revolution bending over a casualty with a gun on her shoulder. The corporal was not unaffected by the feminine charms her bending attitude revealed. His fingers worked, but he controlled himself—once bitten.

Our hostess straightened up, dug a hole in the potato with a pointed knife and drew the thread through it. Then she fixed the potato like a stopper in the neck of the bottle, the contents of which, judging by the smell, could only be one thing—Russian gasolene. Finally she shook the bottle carefully and lit the end of the wick that protruded from the potato. With a proud look at me she pushed the finished lamp into the center of the table, as if to say, "There, you see! Russian soldier girls can deal with any situation."

The corporal and the private settled down to do what all Russian soldiers do when something has gone wrong for them, or when they can't think of any other way of passing the time. They started writing letters. Having carefully moistened the tips of their pencils with their tongues, they bent over the papers with deep, thoughtful furrows in their brows and wrote away. Abbott and Costello had written a lot of letters in the apartment, but I had never seen them receive any. I had an idea that most of the letters which the Russians so purposefully started on never got any further. In reality it was not so much correspondence as a strong urge for release through the written word, in a people that, measured by generations, had only just started school. The art of writing was a valued gift to them, and they never tired of it.

I dug out *The Franco-Prussian War* from my suitcase and started looking through it. I stopped at random on a page with a map of the battlefield of Gravelotte and began to study it—it would do as well as the next thing.

The corporal and the private were diligently at work on their letters. The hostess squatted on her haunches by the fireplace cleaning her carbine. Every now and then, when the wick threatened to burn down, she would pull a bit more out of the potato. The fire crackled, and the lamp smoked and smelt. The cozy atmosphere of a Sunday at home settled heavily and drowsily over the room.

The private and I were shown some berths in a small room separated from another room by a thin wooden partition. Just before falling asleep, I heard someone enter the room next door. A heavy metal object clattered to the floor followed a moment later by the thump of a pair of boots. Then there were a lot of little giggling exclamations interrupted by hushing and tittering. Finally I heard another pair of boots fall heavily to the floor. My last thought before falling asleep was that Russian soldier girls certainly knew how to handle any situation—with or without a carbine.

Next morning I was rudely awakened when the corporal charged into the room and told me to get dressed and ready as quickly as possible. He was beaming all over his face, as if he had had a lovely dream or something even better.

I suppressed my envy and yawningly explained that getting ready was mainly a question of waking up properly, but the corporal could not be bothered to listen. He had something to tell which seemed a great deal more amusing to him. Eagerly he explained that he had never before experienced two such fortunate coincidences. One of them he forgot to tell me in his hurry, but I could guess what he meant. The other was that there was a truck parked outside going to Mag-de-burg! Didn't I find that a lucky chance? Then we need not do any more walking.

When we got outside, he pointed at the autobahn, where an

open truck was standing, packed with Russian soldiers. Every inch of the floor space was occupied. The soldiers in the outer rows jutted obliquely outwards like the supports of an overloaded timber transport.

"How do you think we are going to get on that?" I asked dubiously, thinking how much room I alone would take up.

The corporal grinned. "There's room for a whole battalion yet," he said. "You ought to see a Russian truck that's really full!"

I spotted our food haversack hanging halfway outside the backboard. The private was astride the part that was inside the truck. He waved to us like a horseman enjoying his morning ride on a fat, well-fed horse. The corporal climbed up on the backboard. The passengers started cursing and swearing but without any sting to their invectives. It sounded more like something that was customary. When the corporal had finally settled himself in, he reached down a hand to pull me up. The protest from the assembly rose to a chorus of howls. The corporal ignored them, wedged his feet against the backboard and pressed his back into the wall of humanity behind him. In this way he finally succeeded in getting me and my suitcase on board, accompanied by increasingly violent protests as the pressure was relayed along the truck.

In the next instant we drove off. The hostess stood in the door of the log cabin. The barrel of her carbine glittered in the morning sun. The chorus of howls against me changed to a series of irregular whistles in her honor.

# chapter fifteen

We moved at great speed down the autobahn, one of those wide gray concrete bands that had once made it easy for Hitler to concentrate troops for assaults on neighboring states, but now in turn served the Allies as first-class roads leading to the heart of Germany. There was a lot of Russian traffic on the autobahn. I wondered why the drivers of the oncoming trucks were wearing such bad-tempered expressions. Some of them waved a warning hand as if advising us to turn around, but nobody on our truck took any notice. It was not until we had pulled up on the edge of a yawning chasm and looked down on the ruins of a blown-up viaduct, one of the last achievements of the S.S., that we understood the warnings of those who had tried the trip before us.

We headed the other way, and now it was our turn to wave in warning but without affecting the oncoming stream of traffic. It was strange to see this unbroken line of vehicles that, day after day, as if in keeping with some crazy schedule headed straight for nowhere. What a lot of gas they could have saved if some bright guy had planted a little sign a few miles down the road: Autobahn blocked!

There was at least one Russian in our truck who showed complete disregard for the gasolene reserves of the Red Army. He got his own fun out of waving on the unsuspecting drivers with shouts of encouragement towards the hole in the road, while his comrades were just as busy waving them back. This broad-shouldered Russian, who was wearing a crumpled, dirty uniform, left a notable trail of traffic chaos in our wake. He roared with laughter every time he lured one of the oncoming drivers into the trap, but there was no spite in his laughter, only profound satisfaction. He put his whole soul into this foolish project, as a man who will go to any extreme to put over a practical joke.

He was with two friends whose uniforms had the same deranged look as his. They differed from the other men inasmuch as there had been made plenty of room around them, so that they could sit down with their feet up on the backboard. Apparently these three had the upper hand in the truck. They were the ones who cracked all the jokes and graciously accepted the ensuing applause.

When we finally left the autobahn and continued along small, bumpy roads, where we didn't meet a single vehicle to send into the trap, the broad-shouldered Russian turned towards me and started scrutinizing me closely, as if he had reckoned all along that I would come in handy when things got too dull. I had been afraid of this for some time, like the timid train passenger who braces himself for the unpleasant attentions of an inebriated fellow traveler. But his eyes were like his laughter, cheeky and mocking rather than spiteful.

"Who are you?" he shouted up at me.

"Amerikansky," I replied cockily.

"Amerikansky fine!" he said and gave the truck's backboard a loving kick. It was a Studebaker, practically new and practically worn-out. He flashed me a wide grin that made one corner of his mouth run into a red scar, zigzagging down his cheek. The way he held his head made his grin terrible to look at. It seemed to stretch from one ear to the other. I tried to avoid looking at the scar and sent him a grateful smile on behalf of myself and Mr. Studebaker, relieved to have been accepted by the most important guy on the truck. I had no doubt that he saw a kindred spirit in me. My clothes were as rumpled as his and my beard stubbles were even longer.

All morning we continued going west along the small roads, driving through little German villages that looked both poverty-stricken and deserted. There was not a living soul on the roads, no animals in the fields; we had the whole spring landscape to ourselves. I was getting into the right excursion spirit, and when my old fear and uneasiness occasionally returned like the jar of a dentist's drill hitting a partly exposed nerve, I glanced suspiciously first at the sun and then in the direction of the scar-faced Russian. Each time I was relieved to find them both where they should be.

Later in the morning, when both the corporal and I had started looking wistfully at our ration haversack, we reached a village which looked as desolate as all the others we had passed, but was bigger and in a better state of repair. Scar Face made a sign which passed from man to man along the truck and ended as a violent series of thumps on the driver's cab. We pulled up in the middle of the village street. A young lieutenant, who had been sitting up front with the driver, came down to the backboard and started talking to the three Russians, who, far from being impressed, remained seated and answered his questions with a rather superior air. At last they got up lazily, stretched and jumped down from the truck. I looked inquisitively at their uniforms to see what special distinctions these privates could be wearing, since they treated a superior officer in such an offhanded way. I looked and looked but could find neither medals nor badges of proficiency—not a single decoration. But on their faded and dirty tunics I did see several patches and stripes of a lighter color which suggested that, at some time or other, they had been extremely well supplied with all manner of badges. I gave it up.

The three Russians were given a machine gun each, which they carried carelessly over their arms as they strolled grinning down the village street that gleamed white in the afternoon sun. The laughter of the Russians resounded among the farmhouses, which lay dark and uninviting, as if they had been uninhabited for the past two hundred years. It was like a plague-stricken ghost town, where no man had dared to come since. I could see before me the brown, dried-up bodies under the heavy farmhouse bolsters, and it struck me what a grand spot these revered peasants had chosen for their final rest, here underneath the tall trees that held whispering conversations on time and eternity and the transient quality of things.

My straying thoughts were rudely interrupted by three sharp cracks. The three Russians had chosen a farmhouse each just by the roadside and had shattered the front door locks with shots of such easy accuracy as can only come from long training. Then they put their shoulders to the doors and tumbled into the houses. For a short moment, rustic peace returned to the scene, but then the farms woke to life as if touched by some magic wand. Out of the doors poured not ancient shriveled mummies, but very much alive and terrified Germans. I was shaken by the contrast between the complete peace of one moment and the wild panic of the next, but the Russians in the truck found it vastly amusing and roared with laughter.

When finally the houses had given up all their human content, the three Russians reappeared in their respective doorways like three enormous blowflies who have had the larder all to themselves. Their arms were full of foodstuff, which they gingerly carried over to the truck, where they threw it over the backboard, climbed after it and once more sat down on the floor, surrounded by mounds of sausages, hams, meat and bread.

Scar Face triumphantly held up a cake to show the others, but he dropped it a second later with a vicious oath. The cake was just out of the oven and steaming hot.

The return of the three Russians was the signal for a general disembarkation from the truck. The lieutenant and my corporal disappeared into a building which I guessed would be the inn, and the privates spread around to smaller farms in the outskirts of the village. The same scene was repeated. Farm after farm jumped to life. The village was thoroughly and methodically looted not only of its food but also clothes, trinkets, household goods and the strangest utensils which the Russians had suddenly fallen for.

A fine drizzle of rain started falling. Suddenly my corporal seemed to remember something. He jumped off the truck, shouted to the driver that he would only be a minute and started running towards one of the farms. His unfamiliar burst of speed told me there must be something unusually important going on.

The inhabitants of the village had already started back towards their farms, but seeing the corporal running their way they huddled together in terror once more. Probably they were remembering certain details of the German campaign in Russia and feared that the corporal had been ordered to set fire to the village.

I was right. When the corporal exerted himself as far as to run, it was because of something important. He came out of the farmhouse in a flash of colors. In each hand he carried a half-opened lady's umbrella, one blue with white dots and the other red. Two cotton umbrellas in cheap, gaudy colors.

Panting and out of breath, the corporal clambered up the backboard with his prizes. The truck started and he squeezed down beside me on the floor where I had remained, under the personal protection of the scar-faced Russian. When the corporal had recovered some of his strength he commenced a careful and critical survey of the respective merits of the two umbrellas. He folded them up, unfurled them again and held them up, letting his eyes wander from one to the other. It was still raining, but the corporal took his time. At last his considerations seemed to have led him to a decision, for he handed me the red umbrella with an expression that told me it grieved him deeply not to be able to have both umbrellas open at the same time. I thanked him profusely.

For a while we sat letting the rain beat a tattoo on the umbrellas. The corporal twisted and turned as much as the space would allow. Obviously there was something bothering him. He kept sending quick appraising glances from one umbrella to the other, his eyes lingering more and more on my magnificent red one. Suddenly he seemed to lose control of himself. With a quick movement he snatched the red umbrella out of my hands and handed me the blue polka-dotted one in its place. He peered at me shyly, and I indicated with a nod that I was perfectly satisfied with the deal. Shortly afterwards the rain stopped, but the corporal remained sitting under his red canopy.

On and on we drove, down one small road after the other, apparently without any set destination or purpose. I asked my scar-faced pal, "When do we hit Magdeburg?"

He waved his hand with a grin. "Tomorrow, or the day after—or next year." There was no doubt that he was completely indifferent as to where he would get to and when. He yawned contentedly, leaned his back against the forest of legs behind him, pulled his cap down over his eyes and let things come as they might.

Around evening we came to another German village, where we stopped to spend the night. The population had obviously been visited by similar expeditions and had very probably little left to lose, for they made no attempt to lock their doors or to hide. The only thing they had found worth concealing was their young girls. There was not a single one among the dark groups gathered around the farm gates or on the front porches. Scar Face and his two companions helped me and our haversack of rations down from the truck and, with the corporal and the private following at a respectful distance, we started a reconnaissance of the farms to find the best quarters for the night.

Most of the houses were already occupied by three or four soldiers from the truck. Many of them had flopped down on the huge peasant beds, still wearing boots and full equipment. There they lay giving orders to the Germans whom they had set to work preparing meals. In one of the barnyards we encountered a Russian, who staggered under the burden of a large white bird. His obvious pride in this possession told us that he thought it was a goose. The enticing fowl was, in fact, nothing less than a swan, which he had caught in the village pond. The swan's loud and energetic protests against this unflattering misunderstanding did not have the slightest effect on the Russian.

Eventually we halted at a small farm, where the farmer received us without a word and with a grim expression on his face. He had probably hoped to the very last that he would somehow be passed over this time. In the rooms practically all items that were not permanent fixtures had been removed. Only the faded rectangles on the wallpaper revealed that these bare and dismal rooms might once have had a more inviting atmosphere.

Next morning the truck passengers gathered once more like a party of travelers rested and ready for new adventures. Before we left, new mark notes printed in Russia were issued in the village street as payment for board and lodging. The inhabitants received the notes with the same dubious look as the barber at Templehof. Apparently they hadn't improved in value since then.

Presently we left the small roads and joined the highway to Magdeburg. It was teeming with people and vehicles, and as we progressed the side roads poured new crowds onto the highway that was eventually reduced to a narrow white strip between the two broad churning streams of traffic on either side. In the middle the Russian transport convoys, which our truck had joined, drove towards the heart of Germany, each vehicle filled like ours with a cargo of fresh and enterprising Russian troops. Shouts and greetings flew from truck to truck, as if the whole mile-long convoy was one big family picnic.

No one in the convoy paid the slightest attention to the dismal frame surrounding it. In the fields along the roadside there was a compact wall of defeated German soldiers on their way east. An army completely dissolved, shattered.

My corporal anxiously patted his pockets to make sure he still had my papers. We finally pulled up by a Russian girl soldier, who was pretending to direct the traffic. She looked through my papers, and to my great dismay she pointed away from the road. The corporal jumped back on the truck but was obviously preparing to abandon it for good. He fastened his folded, red umbrella to the haversack and when we had been driven a bit farther down the road, he signalled me that we were getting off.

"Where are we going now?" I asked the corporal as the three of us, the private lugging the haversack on his back, once more wandered on foot down the road, while the truck disappeared towards Magdeburg.

He misunderstood the question. "We are not going very far," he said consolingly. "The worst of it is over now."

"You are going to be handed over in that village over there," he said shortly afterwards and turned down the side road.

"Why don't we go directly to the reception camp at Mag-de-burg?" I asked. The feeling of being on a picnic had vanished.

"I only know what it says in your papers," he answered indifferently.

Yes, and I'm not so sure you know that much, I thought furiously. Was this Russian journey to continue along the lines of an obstruction race to the very end? Or had some playful Russian officer planned it like one of these party games, where you throw a six and triumphantly move right up near the goal, only to find that you land on a square that sends you all the way back again.

"Show me those papers," I said and put my hand out for them. "There must be some mistake."

He edged away from me. "I have orders to hand you over here. It says so quite clearly in the papers," he said stubbornly.

I could do nothing with him. He was determined to avoid any situation that might mean the slightest difficulty for him.

We continued down to the village school, where the corporal with intense relief handed me over to a captain, who had established headquarters in one of the classrooms. The captain scratched down a sort of receipt for me on a piece of paper and gave it to the corporal, whereupon the corporal and I very coolly took leave of each other. He hurried out to get back on the highway as quickly as possible with his wandering party and hitch a ride back to Berlin.

The captain looked through my papers, placed the inevitable stamps here and there, and told me politely but with finality that I would have to spend the night in this village. Tomorrow I would be escorted to Magdeburg.

I left the captain, who was already bending over some new papers (a comforting sign), and went out through the door followed by a new guard. These ubiquitous guards that always appeared from nowhere! While we wandered down the narrow village street that was filled with a mixed fragrance of manure and flowering chestnut trees, I tried to remember how long it was since I had ceased being an individual. I felt myself the victim of some quaint ethnographical joke. An American as the Siamese twin of an endless chain of different Russians.

The night quarters I shared with the guard were situated in a large, neat house that looked like a doctor's residence. We were shown two rooms on the ground floor. They were clean and aired and lacked that dusty and deserted appearance I was used to from my previous apartments. The guard sat in one room and I in the other. He was very young and looked like a nice fellow, but all of a sudden I felt sick to death of being stared at like some strange animal, and I wished he would take his eyes off me.

Someone had dragged a great heavy eiderdown into the room, and I went to bed beneath it on a kind of bench. I soon fell asleep and dreamed about all the young girls I had known or wished to know—all united in the one I had left behind in Stockholm months ago. As far as I remember it was not a very nice dream.

I woke up once during the night and happened to look into the other room, where I saw a large, white disc. It was some time before I could convince myself in my semiconscious state that it was neither the moon nor any other heavenly body strayed in through the window, but that it was in fact the guard, who had gone to bed on the sofa after carefully removing his precious S.S. breeches and placing them neatly folded on the floor beside him. Shivering, I crept well down under my own covers and fell asleep again.

# chapter sixteen

I almost danced in front of my guard the next morning on the way to the school. The busy captain had my papers ready and having proved his efficiency even at that early hour by whacking on a few extra-large stamps, he shouted an order to a young lieutenant in a front room. The lieutenant disappeared, while the guard and I sat like good children at two of the classroom desks. The captain made polite excuses because he did not have the time to converse with me. The stamps thumped down and the fountain pen spluttered. All in all a confidence-inspiring picture of organization and efficiency.

When at last the lieutenant returned, the guard and I followed him outside the school building, where a little green delivery van was drawn up; a four-cylinder Opel, vintage 1925, one of those almost fossilized cars that will never wear out. It had been painted green, an unpleasant murky shade applied with a brush that had been held in a hand either unskilled or else completely indifferent. Beneath the thin coat of paint I could trace various stages of its eventful life, a sort of synopsis of the history of Germany during the preceding years. Standing out most clearly was the word AMBULANCE, smeared along the side of the van with clumsy, hurried lettering. Just beneath it was the word EMERGENCY CAR and under that again AIR RAID PRECAUTION SERVICE almost obliterated. But of course it was a long time since that institution had functioned in Germany. Behind all the other words, you could by means of archaeological scrutiny make out the words STEIN'S BÄCKEREI, but they had almost completely disappeared like most German prewar memories.

The guard opened the back doors leading into the hold of baker Stein's former bread-van and scrambled inside with his machine gun. The lieutenant got behind the wheel, and I sat beside him with my little suitcase at my feet.

We started off. The lieutenant was in fine spirit. He whistled, and I beat time with my foot. It was impossible to keep still. The last day! Forgotten were the compounds in Berlin, the wall-of-death driving round the skeleton streets of the ruined city, forgotten was Red Eyes and the perspiring captain, all left back there in the gray mist, the icy damp fingers of which I hoped I should never feel again. Forgotten was everything except the last efficient thump of the stamp on my papers, my ticket to freedom, contained in the lieutenant's little case lying on the seat between us.

He must have noticed that I could hardly contain myself, for he smiled understandingly. "Glad to be getting home?" he said.

I gave him a friendly pat on the shoulder. "Yeah, I've had enough of war for now!"

And for the rest of my life, I added to myself. Now to get away from it all! To spend the next few months in a hammock between tall, shady trees, gazing up into the foliage and listening to the bees, grasshoppers and birds. Neither reading nor writing; not even speaking to too many, preferably to no one of the male sex and certainly not to anyone in uniform. A small table by the side of the hammock with a bottle of real whisky and, perhaps, a single bottle of soda. Empty the whisky and start on another. Thinking of nothing at all. Try to brush off the war, as a snake sheds its dirty old skin, and find my own civilian self again. Sure, I was glad to be getting home.

"I don't expect you're sorry it's all over?" I asked the lieutenant. He shook his head.

"Well, let's get the last part over in a hurry. There's no need to waste time saying good-bye to it," I added jokingly.

The lieutenant grinned and increased the speed. He shouldn't have done that, for in the next moment our right front wheel was buried deep in the ditch at the side of the road, and the little van tilted dangerously with two wheels in the air. The lieutenant got out and that made the van keel over still further. I heard the guard's machine gun slide across the floor, clattering against some other metal object. I crept out carefully. The lieutenant stood crestfallen looking at the ruins of his reputation as a driver.

"Aren't you used to driving?" I asked.

He shook his head. "No, I've only just learned it here in Germany. Usually I manage fine," he added with an expression suggesting that he tested prototype racers every day, "but this goddamned old money box. . . ." He sent the little green van a withering glare.

I gave appropriate instructions and aided by the guard we soon got the lieutenant's money box back on the road. He worried the gears as if he were dealing with a tough and cunning adversary, and drove on carefully. I felt sorry for the green van that was not to blame for the accident, and I decided that it might be well to give the lieutenant a few practical hints on driving.

We turned onto the highway at the spot where I had taken leave of my three degraded protectors, and were soon swallowed up by the traffic.

Magdeburg was beginning to stretch out its antennae of ruins towards us, and soon we could see the city's broken profile like a charcoal sketch on the blue sky ahead. I was just trying to work out whether my first drink should be an Old-fashioned or a straight bourbon, when the cars in front of us came to a complete standstill. We pulled up, too, right in the middle of a long line of vehicles.

"Control post," the lieutenant informed me laconically and leaned back in the seat with the fatalism of a Russian resigning himself to a long and inevitable wait. He picked up the case lying between us, took out my papers and started looking at them.

"You come from Berlin?" he asked. I reacted automatically, straining all my senses to detect the slightest hint of suspicion in his voice. But I could find nothing more than kind interest. He pushed the papers back in the case and began to tell me where he came from, starting with true Russian disregard of accurate geography on the long and gruelling trail from Stalingrad to Berlin, which all Russians seem to have covered.

At last it was our turn. The lieutenant grabbed his case and disappeared into the guard hut. A moment later he came back again. "Everything okay; we're going on."

"Is this the last control post before Magdeburg?" I asked hopefully.

He shook his head good-naturedly—what could this foreigner know of Russian organizational talent? "Are you crazy? There are at least three or four more!"

We drove on, the lieutenant with his eyes fixed stiffly on the road and the wheel gripped tightly between his hands. Watching for some indication that we were getting near our destination, I passed as briefly as possible over some enormous pens full of ragged men and women. Most of them shuffled aimlessly around inside the barbed-wire fencing, many lay prostrate on the ground too weak to move. A thin line had formed at the fence to watch the traffic on the highway.

"Are they Germans going east?" I asked the lieutenant.

He looked over at the pens. "That's a transit camp for Russian D.P.'s," he said without further comment.

Fortunately other things appeared to command the whole of my attention—large signs with the legend "Prisoners of War" and arrows pointing towards Magdeburg. Those English words removed my last doubts. We must be getting very close to the American camp.

I decided not to worry any more, but to settle down and enjoy the last part of the trip. We passed through two more control posts without incident, but at the next one I thought the lieutenant stayed suspiciously long in the hut. Reluctantly the thinking machine started again. With an almost physical tiredness I felt the little cog wheels up there grinding together. When the lieutenant came out, I thought I could read confusion in his eyes.

"Queer!" he said, and put down the case with my papers. "It seems we're not going any farther along the highway. This is the last control post, but they say your papers aren't like the usual permits. They daren't take the responsibility. We've got to get the last stamp at some bigger post. They say it's ten minutes' run down this way." He waved his hand towards a side road that went in a direction opposite to the arrows pointing to the P.O.W. camp.

I gripped the seat tightly, like an airplane passenger who has been flying for a long time in bright sunshine, but runs into a thick, brown fog-soup above the airport and has to land at the bottom of the dish.

"It's a damn nuisance," the lieutenant said, expressing my thoughts for me. "But it will only be a formality. Probably it's just because your papers are too good."

The control post was a log cabin with two armed guards in front of the entrance. The lieutenant took his case and went inside. He stayed even longer than the previous time, and finally he came out with a police officer, who was carrying my papers. The police officer subjected me to a close scrutiny, referring to the papers as if I were a dangerous, wanted criminal. Then he gave the lieutenant some order in a low voice and handed him the papers.

After some tricky maneuvering, he managed to get the van turned around and we drove back the way we had come.

"I don't get it," said the lieutenant and gave me a quizzical look. "Nobody seems to want to accept responsibility for your case." Suspicion and respect fought for supremacy in his expression. Then the respect won. "You must be a big shot," he said.

I gave him a confidential look, and he nodded as if he understood.

"I've got orders to report to headquarters," he said, proudly swerving to avoid a large stone in the road. "I hope they have some more sense there than these yokels on the highway."

I decided to play the part the lieutenant had inadvertently but most conveniently found for me. The Very Important Person to whom stamps are ridiculous trifles and this driving from one control post to the other a stupid formality to be remembered later with great amusement. On no account must the lieutenant be allowed to feel that the important person was getting very uneasy or that he had no means to get to the bottom of the mystery. I felt the old familiar tingle of excitement and nervousness under my skin.

"Phew! Isn't there a queer smell in here?" I said and sniffed the air distastefully.

There was really an exceptionally vile smell in the cab, as if all the exhaust from the engine had gathered in this small compartment.

All the lieutenant's senses had been occupied with driving. Now he sniffed too and nodded. "Yes, there's a hell of a stink. Smells like a sewer. Do you think there might be something wrong with the car?"

One of the few things in this world I really know something about is cars. Not only can I identify practically all existing models, but I also have a fair idea of what lies under their hoods. It's been a hobby with me since I was a kid. I've always been laughed at and called car-crazy. But what could be more natural than for me, in this situation where everything was hanging by a thin thread, to grasp at one thing I really knew something about and hope to find some inspiration there.

The lieutenant stopped the car.

"Let's have a look at the engine," I said and walked up to the hood. The lieutenant followed me, and the guard came out of the back with his machine gun carelessly cradled in his arms.

"Motor okay, *njet?*" he exclaimed, with a proud grin at his newly acquired American language.

"Motor *njet* okay," I said, holding my nose.

I opened one side of the hood. The two Russians bent forward with great interest, looking down into the powerful engine's mysterious jumble of pipes and leads.

"Know anything about cars?" I asked the lieutenant, not so much for the sake of the question as to establish a fact.

He shook his head in embarrassment. "I can only drive them," he answered with a bold exaggeration of the truth. "But I'll get the hang of it some time!" He sent a challenging look down into the mystic depths.

On top of the cylinders were some small valves, through which you could release the engine exhaust—an ancient and long-obsolete system. Quickly I opened one of the valves. It gave out a small hissing sound, and a dense, concentrated stench rose to meet us. The two Russians hastily drew back as I let the gasses out of the other valves. They looked at me with eyes full of admiration and wonder because, without a moment's hesitation, I had found the right spot even in this chaos of engine parts. Besides being a Very Important Person I was obviously an expert on motor cars.

We aired out the cab, and then continued down the side road to the highway. We came to the control post, where the lieutenant showed the sentry outside the hut a new slip of paper, which cleared us right away to headquarters. More and more "Prisoners of War" signs appeared. Old man Tantalus can't have suffered more than I did, as the signs slipped past my eyes. They told all American prisoners of war and internees to report to a camp down by the river Elbe.

Five minutes later we turned down another side road wider than the last one and also equipped with P.O.W. signs and arrows. We were in the outskirts of Magdeburg, and I carefully memorized all the characteristic features of the countryside. We passed the ruins of a house, where a small lane ran into our road from a large open area. Shortly afterwards we passed another lane running into our road. Four or five miles down this lane in the direction of Berlin, there was a belt of shrubbery, and then forest. I didn't stop to think what I was going to use this seemingly pointless geographical survey for, but I automatically imprinted the road and its two lanes on my mind like an ordnance map.

Finally we came to a large gray building with Russian military vehicles parked at the entrance. Once more the lieutenant picked up his case and with the resigned expression of a salesman who knows nobody is going to like his samples, he disappeared through the great gloomy entrance.

A long time went by. I got fed up with waiting in the cab and walked round to the back of the van, where the guard sat dangling his legs.

"What's been rattling about in here?" I asked and peered into the semidarkness of the compartment.

Indolently the guard twisted halfway round and pointed. "That thing! Gets me down, too. What do we want it for, anyway?"

It was an empty jerry can. What did we want that for? Unless we might be going back to. . . . and we carried the jerry can in case we should want gasolene on the way.

I fought as hard as I could, but I couldn't prevent my thoughts forming the word "Berlin." I shuddered.

At last the lieutenant came out. He screwed up his eyes as if he had been blinded by the sudden change from semidarkness to hard, white sunlight. Or was there something he didn't understand? At any rate he wasn't bringing good news. He walked slowly, staring perplexedly at my papers, as if trying to find some reason in a matter that seemed utterly absurd to him.

"I don't get it!" he said, opening the van door. He got behind the wheel and once more studied the forms one by one. He shook his head. His efforts at understanding only seemed to increase his perplexity.

"The devil himself couldn't make head or tail of this," he finally said hopelessly. "The orders"—he pointed to the papers which the efficient captain had given him that morning and which were liberally decorated with authentic looking stamps—"are that you are to be taken directly to the P.O.W. camp at the Elbe. There can be no doubt whatsoever about that. But in there they say"—he waved a hand at the building—"in there they say that there has been a change of orders and that I have to take you back to Berlin without delay." He showed me a new form on which were a few lines of meticulous writing.

He looked at me appealingly. Fortunately he did not—as most other people would have—take out his irritation on the innocent victim, but on the fools at the control posts, who didn't seem to know what the hell they wanted. That was the only consolation for me.

I sat in my seat as the embodiment of twentieth century man equipped with snatches of knowledge on a thousand different unimportant matters, but helpless as a child in the darkness when seeking the answer to a few simple questions about his personal fate in the hands of mystical and impersonal powers.

"Then you don't mind if we turn around and drive back to Berlin?" the lieutenant interrupted my thoughts.

I shrugged my shoulders and smiled. "If we hurry I might get there in time for supper with general Shukoff," I said jokingly but in a tone that left the lieutenant in some doubt as to whether

I might be serious. I looked around quickly, as if impatient to get started. I was in fact once more memorizing the features of the landscape, the side road we were driving on, the two lanes, the ruined house and the spot where the P.O.W. signs with their arrows started. The lieutenant turned the van and started off slowly.

"By the way," I said, taking care not to sound too enthusiastic, "why go back along this road? I have a map of Berlin." I pointed to my suitcase. "Let's see if we can take a short cut."

The lieutenant nodded. Apparently that was a good idea. I opened the suitcase and, screened behind the lid, I started running through *The Franco-Prussian War*, in which I knew there was a map of the battlefield at Gravelotte. There was little danger of the lieutenant's eyes leaving the road, but if it should happen, a map of Gravelotte A.D. 1871 would be better than no map at all.

"Now let's see," I said, looking from the Magdeburg district down to the victorious German positions on the old battlefield, "if we take the road there on the left"—I pointed to the first lane we would get to—"and continue a good way down it, then we will arrive here." My finger stopped at the church in Gravelotte, the only civilian feature on the map, while my eyes followed the lane running into the forest four or five miles ahead. There were no buildings before the forest. What lay beyond it time alone would tell. "From there the lane joins the highway. We save at least fifteen minutes' driving," I said triumphantly, and snapped the suitcase shut.

"That's fine," said the lieutenant. "It's only twelve o'clock. We should make Berlin by evening."

That was the only thing I was completely certain we would not do. Absolutely and calmly sure. Where we would get to, and which of us would get there, I didn't know yet. But one thing was certain: I wouldn't get to Berlin that evening.

We turned left down the lane. It was a long time since a motor car had been here. The lieutenant cursed this and all similar roads that had made his life a misery during the preceding five years. I said yes and no and cursed in the right places, while my head was teeming with plans of escape. But it was all waste steam, through which I could just discern confused scenes from novels I had read and films I had seen. I decided to turn off the steam and concentrate instead on my only three advantages: the lieutenant's notion that there was nothing suspicious about my return to Berlin, his and the guard's respect for me as an expert on motor cars and finally my sense of direction. These three factors must in the decisive moment fit together like the pieces in a jig-saw puzzle. The only snag was that I had to construct the puzzle first. And time was getting short.

The forest was cool, and the soft light seeping through the trees was restful to the eyes. I said nothing for another mile, but I kept a sharp look out for a small road that would connect the lane we were driving on, with the one running parallel to it by the ruined house. A couple of hundred yards ahead I spotted a thinning out in the trees that might mean a crossroad. I wrinkled my nose and sniffed. "I think we've got engine trouble again," I said.

The bumpy forest road had sorely tried the lieutenant's skill as a driver. He slowed up. "Better have a look at it again," he said with relief.

I stretched lazily in the seat. "Wouldn't it be a good idea to have some lunch?" I asked.

The lieutenant suddenly found that he, too, was hungry. He pulled up and we both got out and walked round to the back of the van, where the guard was sitting like a mascot between the two open doors.

"We're hungry," the lieutenant declared.

A moment later all three of us were sitting on the edge of the ditch, fraternally sharing some bread and German sausage. I ate without appetite, feeling solemn and almost devout. Whatever happened this would be my last meal with the Russians. The lieutenant and the guard were unwitting participants in a farewell banquet. I was almost sorry that I couldn't make a moving little speech in which I told them that without their touching faith in me, I should now be on my way back to my prison in Berlin, but thanks to them I would instead, within the next hour, be moving the other way.

While I chewed the bread and sausage slowly, the rough draft of a plan formed in my mind. The details would have to wait until the moment when the plan would be launched. Strangely enough I didn't feel the least bit nervous. The loud NO that had resounded through my mind when the lieutenant told me we had been ordered back to Berlin was in some inexplicable way not only my own order to myself, but at the same time an unknown voice that promised to help me.

I stretched out in the grass and rested my head against a tree trunk. I had been right, the thinning out of the trees two hundred yards ahead was a crossroad. The road on the right, which I would use, seemed to be as wide as the one we were on now, and would thus accommodate a motor car. There was every reason to assume that it joined up with the lane I was especially interested in—the one that came out by the ruined house. Once I had gone that far, I would be past all the control posts and only had to follow the signs with the arrows to reach the American camp. . . . But before I got that far, there were a lot of things to straighten out.

The guard started putting the food away. His machine gun, the most important piece of the jig-saw puzzle, was flapping carelessly at his side.

I strolled over to the van, opened the hood, bent down over the engine and sniffed its bad breath. I twiddled and manipulated the various movable parts, importantly wiping off some dirt here and there. The lieutenant followed all my movements breathlessly. The engine was okay, but I took care to make my face express increasing anxiety. Finally I unscrewed the radiator cap and peered down the tank. There was absolutely no reason to doubt that there was plenty of water. The engine had worked beautifully all morning, apart from the unpleasant smell which was a constructional peculiarity no one could alter. The little green van was in every way serviceable and ready to start.

I turned towards the lieutenant pessimistically. "We can't get any farther," I said. "There's no water in the radiator. Come and have a look yourself."

The lieutenant peered down the dark aperture. He could have made sure in a second that there was plenty of water for several hours of driving; instead his face took on a vaguely offended look. That car was and would remain no damn good. He had not forgotten its deceitful behavior earlier that day.

My first little bluff came off. The lieutenant did what most people would do at such a time—he let his eyes wander in all directions, as if he expected to find a bucket of water hanging on the nearest tree. Now it was just a matter of getting him to make a certain suggestion himself.

"If only there were a river or a stream somewhere near," he said finally.

"What good would that do?" I answered gloomily. "We can't drag the van down to the stream, and we can't carry the stream up here in our hands—"

The guard interrupted me eagerly.

"No, but we've got the jerry can! Don't you remember? It's in the compartment at the back."

"Of course. We can use that," the lieutenant approved.

I pretended to be annoyed that I hadn't thought of it myself. It was all going far easier than I had expected. There was no need for any drastic or dramatic measures. Just arrange a little ordinary mishap and let things work themselves out in accordance with the simple rules of everyday life. I could almost stop pulling the strings, for my two puppets jumped readily and of their own accord into the roles I had planned for them. But I took great care not to show any exultance and kept up my assumed bad-tempered expression. I was the expert who is vexed because two smarter brains have beaten him to an idea.

"What's the use of a jerry can, when we still have no water?" I protested. "We can't go exploring all over the countryside without anything to go by."

The guard and the lieutenant once more hung their heads. The thought didn't appeal to them either.

Suddenly I pretended that I had thought of something bright.

"The map!" I said. "We've got the map! It must show the waterways around here." The expert had once more taken over command of the situation. "Good thing I remembered it. Get the jerry can out, while I have a look at the map."

The lieutenant and the guard hurried over to the back of the van, while I opened the suitcase and flipped through the pages of the invaluable book. At the same time I took a quick look round the front of the van. It was ready to drive away. On the seat was the lieutenant's little case with my papers. I closed the book, snapped the suitcase shut, placing it right up under the dashboard so it wouldn't be in the way whatever happened.

The lieutenant and the guard were waiting for me with the jerry can between them at the back of the van.

"That was a real stroke of luck," I said with a grin to show them that the expert had been rehabilitated. "What would you do without me?"

I pointed diagonally back among the trees in the direction from which we had come. "You see the hill over there? According to the map there's a small lake just behind it. It will be big enough for us. Bring it up here in the jerry can, but hurry. It's getting late."

I gave the guard a gentle shove, sending him off in the direction I had indicated. Neither he nor the lieutenant showed the slightest hint of suspicion. And why should they? Every step in the events led quite naturally, obviously and in the usual, everyday pattern to the next.

I heard the guard shuffling through fallen leaves and the

clanking sound of the jerry can hitting against the machine-gun barrel. The most important piece of the jig-saw puzzle was about to slip into place by itself.

"Got a cigarette?" I asked. I was ready to subject myself to any trial just to divert him. He dug out a couple of Papyrossi, gave me a light and set fire to his own. Then he sat down on the running board and tilted his head back to get the full benefit of a beam of sunshine projected down through the trees. . . .

When I had finished the smoke, I threw away my cigarette butt and shook the lieutenant gently.

"Listen," I said. "We might as well take the opportunity to look at those valves."

He gave a slight start when I woke him out of his doze, stifled a yawn, grinned and got to his feet.

We took the two paces up to the open hood. I remained standing on the left side and waved the lieutenant over to the other side. He watched with interest as I loosened one of the valves, but he drew back when the little poisonous jet of exhaust came hissing out.

He grinned uncertainly. "It smells and sounds just like a—" He said a word I didn't know, though I had no doubt what it meant.

"Wouldn't you like to try it yourself?" I asked, at the same time stealing a glance at the guard, who was still laboring up the hill. "It's high time you got started if you want to learn something about motor car engines. Now look here." I waved him up to the hood and made him bend right down over the engine. He hesitated just a bit, but I decided to go through with it.

"I'll start the engine to collect all the exhaust gasses just under the valves. Then you can let them out! You got that?" I spoke instructively to keep his interest on the magical little metal objects. "But mind you don't touch them before the engine is running, or you'll run the risk of. . . ."

I didn't finish the sentence but stepped back quickly and got

297

in behind the wheel. I threw a quick glance over my left shoulder and saw the guard on top of the hill, looking around for a lake which was not even marked on the old map of the Gravelotte battlefield. With my fingers on the ignition key and my foot on the accelerator I looked through the windshield to make sure that the lieutenant was still bending over the engine. All I saw was the open hood—then I heard the lieutenant's voice in my ear. "I think it will be better if I start the engine."

He was standing by the door bending towards me. His voice told me what I would find in his eyes. For a second I considered following my original plan and giving the van full throttle, but he would probably cling to the door and try to tear the wheel out of my hands.

I tried to control myself and slowly turned my face towards him. He was staring intensely at me with eyes in which doubt and wonder was slowly giving way to a dawning comprehension of something quite fantastic. My plan was collapsing so suddenly that I hadn't time to pretend. The lieutenant's eyes took on a hard and injured look. . . . There was no way out.

I pushed one leg through the open door as if I were about to change places with the lieutenant. He took a short step backwards but intently followed my slightest movement. I brought the other leg down, putting all my weight on it, to make sure I had a firm foothold. Then I tensed my muscles, and threw all my weight and strength into a violent blow to his jaw.

He staggered backwards across the grass, his arm shielding his face, slipped with one leg down in the ditch, but was up again in a flash. He flung himself at me like a prize fighter going into a clinch to give himself time to recover from a blow. Locked together we crashed into the front of the van. The sharp metal point on top of the radiator dug into the small of my back, and I felt his muscles tighten as he tried to force me backwards. He was young, agile and tough. I only had my commando training to fall back on.

In desperation I summoned up all my reserve of strength,

and with the sharp radiator point digging deeper and deeper into my back I forced him back inch by inch. I could feel his hot breath panting in my face. The pain in my back was unendurable, but it made me put still more force into thrusting him back. Finally, when I had a feeling that the metal point was way inside my guts, I succeeded in straightening up, gulping for air and with a red mist swimming before my eyes.

His hands fumbled for my throat, but I caught his right arm and put a lock on it. Through the dull throbbing in my temples I could hear shouts coming from among the trees. With a determined satisfaction I wrenched his arm round on his back. I felt him giving way. His teeth were gnashing together with pain and fury, as I twisted his arm diagonally upwards behind his back. I had a feeling that the whole forest had come to life and was watching our struggle that echoed resoundingly among the trees. The sound of running feet came closer.

When I had twisted his arm back far enough and felt him searching for a foothold, I gave him a sudden shove and followed it up with another heavy punch to the jaw, which sent him head over heels into the ditch. I heard little, plonking thuds against the tree trunks, but I had no time to worry about them or my adversary any more. I leaped for the van and tumbled, almost insensible, down behind the wheel. I started the engine and jammed the accelerator down to the floorboards. The ancient, green van leaped forward. Every joint in it groaned and creaked, but it kept going. Automatically my hand fumbled for the gear lever, while a hail of bullets whipped viciously into the side of the van.

# chapter seventeen

I clenched my hands tightly round the steering wheel. Rocking and jumping, the van sped over the uneven forest road, and the trees rushed past me as if they were trying to overtake each other in some desperate race. The open radiator hood rattled and clanged in tune with the open doors at the back as I forged ahead to get out of range of the guard's machine gun. Another burst swept into the side of the van as I reached the crossroad. I slowed up for a second to negotiate the sharp turn. When I was well round it, I looked back through the trees. The lieutenant was standing in the middle of the road, a lone pathetic figure wildly waving his arms. I heard yet another couple of bursts being fired a long way off, aimlessly and at random. After that I heard only the knocking of the engine and the blood throbbing in my temples as I roared on, my perspiring hands sticking to the wheel, my body bent forwards as if my weight would give the van added speed.

When I had driven a couple of miles I pulled up for a moment and jumped out. As I fastened the hood and closed the back doors, I took a quick survey of the countryside, fixing it in relation to the features I had memorized on the way out.

Then I started again and a few minutes later I came to a wider lane, which I thought must be the one leading to the ruined house. I relaxed my tense grip on the wheel and slowed down a bit, so as not to be too noticeable if I should meet a car coming in the other direction. But I didn't. I had the whole road to myself.

The green van was coughing and heaving, but it kept going, and soon the road became wider and more even. The forest, where a lieutenant with a sore jaw was probably holding conference with a bewildered private carrying an empty jerry can, lay well behind me to the right. With a bit of luck I would have a couple of hours' start on them. Possibly it was not enough. My whole plan might be hopeless, doomed from the start, but I had had no choice. And that was still the way. All I could do was to improvise—everything rested on chance. I banished all thoughts from my mind except just one: to get the very most out of every minute of my lead.

There was still no traffic or other signs of life when I drew close to the spot where the lane joined up with the road we had traveled on that morning on the way to the Russian headquarters. Just before I reached the ruined house I eased the green van into a field behind one of the charred walls. Quickly I grabbed the lieutenant's case and took my papers from it. Those which had been decorated with stamps that morning, I pushed into my pocket. With a deep sense of satisfaction I tore up the new orders with the nasty-looking, meticulous handwriting. I kicked up some top soil and buried the pieces, a neat little grave for my Russian adventures. As I smoothed out the earth with my foot, I was filled with a strange confidence, like a man at the gambling table who suddenly realizes that his luck has changed, and he's not going to lose any more.

After a quick look in all directions, I lifted the radiator hood again and opened the back doors wide. It was probably quite unnecessary, for the ancient green van already looked like part of the ruins. Then I grabbed my little suitcase and quickly covered the short distance to the crossroad. There I turned left, heading for the spot where I knew I would find the signs with the arrows.

There was no possibility of hiding myself, but anyway I had no reason to do so. I could pass as a German if necessary, or a slave laborer. The fight with the lieutenant had not made my clothes look any worse than they did before. I looked exactly like one of the waste products of the great war, and who was going to be interested in what kind of waste I might be, now that I had passed all the control posts? When I came to the first arrow signs I quickened my pace, until I had a feeling that I was in step with the lieutenant and the guard back in the forest. I could not afford to waste a single second if I wanted to keep my lead.

The signs were getting larger and more frequent, and I realized that I was getting close to the American camp. Determinedly I hurried on among the rubble, my head bent forwards and the little suitcase in one hand, a gray anonymous figure among thousands of others seeking some goal for their travels in the shattered pocket-Babylon of Magdeburg.

I made the last part of the way go more quickly by imagining the welcome awaiting me. Who would receive me? A G.I. I supposed, who would assure me with a drawl that the entire United States army had thought of nothing but the missing Aage Smith for the past month. At the same time the expression of his face would tell me all too clearly that the United States army had a million things to attend to of far greater importance than my dilapidated person.

I was just phrasing some withering sarcasm that would take him down a peg, when I stopped beneath a large sign that told me I was at the transit camp for prisoners of war. I looked around puzzled. I could see no camp, only a low wall surrounding an area that looked like a park with bushes and lawns. I looked along the wall and saw a large iron gate, standing open. Feeling like a little boy in a fairy tale I stood at the iron gate with my suitcase, looking for the castle of the Sleeping Beauty, but all I could see was a wide drive, disappearing into the shrubbery. I felt completely lost as I walked along it, peering in all directions. Had the camp been moved? Was I too late? Had all the other prisoners of war in Europe already been exchanged, while I, the only one left, had been forgotten—homeless and utterly superfluous?

I passed the shrubbery and once more looked eagerly around. My heart turned a somersault and stopped dead for a moment. I averted my face to banish the sight, but when I looked back it was still there, even more real than before. No, I had not been forgotten, I had come home again! The usual reception committee was there to greet me all right.

There was a high barbed-wire fence running round a large section of the park, and in front of the only hole in the barbed wire, armed guards were walking up and down—wearing Russian uniforms. I had come to the end of my journey and was at the same time back where it had started—at a Russian fence. The American P.O.W. camp at the Elbe was a Russian camp, possibly for Americans, possibly not. I couldn't take it any more. I couldn't all at one time keep in mind the captain in Berlin and the lieutenant in the forest—and this. I was through with the whole thing. Let them do their damnedest.

I straightened my back and walked with firm steps over to the hole in the barbed wire, pulled my papers from my pocket and pushed them under the nose of one of the sentries. He looked anxiously at my determined face as if trying to discover why the man with the suitcase, who had looked so peaceful over by the shrubbery, had suddenly turned so angry. Furiously I waved the papers in his face. He took them and looked at the stamps. Then he returned them to me, stepped aside nervously and pointed to a great mansion, lying at the end of the drive. I didn't deign to look at him but set off down the drive like a man who will not tolerate any interference with his affairs.

I hurried up some broad stone steps and stopped at a door, behind which I could hear a hum of voices. For a brief moment I let my hand rest on the heavy doorknob that felt beautifully cool against my palm. Maybe it would be wise to calm down a bit after all. A man in a temper is an easy victim.

I swallowed a lump in my throat and pushed the door open. The quiet hum of voices rose to loud conversation like a radio that has suddenly been turned on full blast. My first impression was of a great hall filled with a lot of people who, with no apparent aim, drifted around in a cloud of cigarette smoke. Most of them turned their heads when the door was opened, but looked indifferently away again, resuming their aimless stroll.

My gaze was halted by a desk, standing away from the walls to the right in the hall. A woman wearing glasses and a Russian uniform was sitting behind it. Around her were three or four young men in American Air Force uniforms. They were leaning over the desk as if they had been engaged in an eager conversation with the woman and had been interrupted when I opened the door. Both the woman and the airmen looked at me. American uniforms! Just what I had dreamed of seeing again for the past month. Without worrying about the woman at the desk I rushed over to the nearest flier and grabbed his hand. "Christ! Am I glad to see you!" I said with a husky voice.

He looked at me with surprise but shook my hand.

I continued in embarrassment, "I mean, you have no idea how happy I am to see some different uniforms! I'm from O.S.S. I've been through the whole show in Berlin. Now I wouldn't mind getting back home."

The woman behind the desk followed our talk with a watchful look behind the lenses.

The airman shook my hand again, this time with more enthusiasm.

"Here's another American wanting to get home—but quick," he said to the woman with the glasses. He put heavy emphasis on the words *but quick*, and I gathered that this was a direct continuation of the talk they had been having when I came in.

"We've been waiting here since yesterday," he went on, turning to me but still addressing the woman behind the desk as well. "And what in hell are we waiting for?" He waved an impatient hand.

The woman nervously shifted her eyes from him to me.

"American officer. Lieutenant in the O.S.S.," I said, handing her my papers.

At the same time another airman bent over the desk and said angrily, "You told us we'd be moving off at one o'clock. Then you swore before God that it certainly wouldn't be later than two. It's after three now! Why don't those trucks turn up? Why don't you do something?"

The woman looked up from my papers with a hunted look in her eyes. "But I have told you, gentlemen—everything has been done to speed up your transport," she said in fluent English. "The trucks will be here any moment. I can understand that you are in a hurry, but you must be patient for just a little while yet."

She tried to concentrate on my papers again.

The airman I had been talking to put his head right down to her.

"Yeah, that's all very well. When you've been a prisoner of war for two years, you're just about to bust—with patience! There are hundreds of trucks in the American camp. Your army has borrowed plenty of them already," he added teasingly. "Why not borrow a couple more for us? The whole thing could be fixed up in ten minutes."

The woman put her hands over her ears in mock despair. "Don't worry! It will be all right!"

The airman pressed his point relentlessly. "Yesterday afternoon at the same time you promised us. . . ."

The woman gave it up. She shook her head, picked up a stamp and placed it as the final touch to all the other stamps my papers had received that morning. Then she handed them back to me and got up from the desk.

"Gentlemen," she said with a hopeless but at the same time indulgent smile, "I assure you that there will be no further delay. If you will all stand by your beds you will shortly be issued rations to take over to your own camp."

The airman and I walked diagonally across the hall, while the woman went from group to group with her message about the rations.

"Is she the only Russian here?" I asked surprised. The airman laughed. "Are you crazy! The whole building is crawling with Russian sentries. She's just a show they've put on, so that we can tell them back home, how nice and tactful they treated us. As far a I can make out she's a security officer and handles the stamps and all that bull. Incidentally she's mighty nice as long as we curse and shout at her, but you should see the others come charging in, if we start sulking and creeping around the dark corners."

I threw a quick look at my new surroundings. There were both soldiers and civilians, not what you'd call a gala representation but still much too fine company for me, I noted with embarrassment. The airmen kept in a group by themselves. They were dressed in varied uniforms, fur-lined leather jackets and other snappy aviation fashions, the somewhat deranged condition of which was more than compensated for by their slightly superior airs. I wondered why my companion, a young, tall, loose-jointed fellow in a leather jacket and fur-lined flying boots, had taken so heartily to someone as hopelessly civilian as myself.

We came to a long corridor with doors leading into various smaller rooms. We went inside one of them, where tiered bunks had been erected up against all the walls.

"My name's Fred," the airman said, taking off his funny little baseball cap and throwing it on one of the lower bunks. "I hope you didn't mind us disturbing your girl friend in there while she was going through your papers. Not because—I mean, naturally they're okay," he added hastily with a twinkle in his eye. "But as a rule you guys from O.S.S. are hot stuff at anything but papers, so I thought that it couldn't do any harm, if we kind of gave you a hand."

I nodded vacantly and not half as gratefully as I had intended, because I was remembering the lieutenant and the guard. They would still be on their way. It was as if a door in my mind had suddenly opened on what lay outside: I heard them once more; hurried steps along a gravel road. And I saw, as through a telescope, the lieutenant's face looming more and more clearly before me, not the naïve, good-natured face, nor the wildly distorted one, but an entirely new lieutenant, determined, purposeful and coldly planning revenge. I stole a glance at my wrist watch. At the very most I still had half an hour's lead. But supposing the hurried steps I heard in my mind were only an echo, supposing the owners of the busy feet had already hitched a ride. . . .

I heard someone coming in and turned around with a start.

"Take it easy," said Fred and grabbed my arm. "It's just some nice presents from the kind lady," he went on, and removed two packages from a huge pile that threatened to force a little Russian soldier down on his knees.

"Thanks Tovaritch," he drawled, giving the Russian a friendly pat on the back. He sat down on the bunk, opened the packages without enthusiasm and pulled out two large loaves of rye bread.

"Tangible expressions of friendship!" he said, weighing a loaf in each hand. "At least we don't have to starve the next couple of days. Let's see if there are more delicacies."

He fetched out a bag, poured some of the contents into his palm, sniffed it and looked up at me with feigned horror in his eyes. Then he let his hand drop and jumped up from the bunk. "What's the matter with you?" he said. "You've gone all white in the face. Is it this Mahorka stuff making you fade out?"

"No, it's just the possibility of having to sit here for days on end nibbling rye bread," I answered with a sickly smile. "Tell me frankly, do you think there's any hope of getting off right away?"

He nodded seriously and started doing up our packages. "Wouldn't say it, if I didn't think so. We've kicked up one hell of a row, like a whole counter-revolution since yesterday. If there's anything I can do for you, just give me the word."

"Yes, tell me where we go from here," I said, hoping that he would drown out the footbeats pounding in my mind. By now they had broken into a brisk run on the last lap towards the gray headquarters.

"Our girl friend in there says we're just going a short way down the Elbe. Then we cross a pontoon bridge to a small island in the middle of the stream. The exchange takes place on that island. Once that's over, we'll be with our own outfit. Then we can settle down and enjoy the ride across another pontoon bridge leading over to our side of the river. And then we're home. Takes no time at all."

I looked at my watch again. On my little private movie screen I saw the lieutenant dashing in, capless and with his uniform disarranged. I saw him burst through the door into a large room and stop breathlessly in front of the first desk he came to, crying, "He got away!"

"Let's go down into the hall ready to move off," Fred suggested. "Don't forget your package. The Russians don't like individualists," he added with an ambiguous smile.

I picked up my suitcase and strolled out into the hall. The woman was sitting behind her desk again, besieged by a new lot of uniforms. The civilians were standing in small groups chatting eagerly. Only a few of them kept to themselves as if they didn't really belong anywhere. Fred's pals were gathered in one corner of the hall carelessly leaning up against the wall and throwing slightly superior bohemian glances at the bourgeoisie in the center of the floor. But they too held their rye bread and Mahorka under one arm, and their eyes moved like those of the other mortals more and more frequently towards the wide entrance. There was a tense and expectant atmosphere in the room.

"Most of them are on the level," said Fred. "But a few of them will have a tough time trying to convince our people on the other side. Take the guy over there for instance."

He gave a barely perceptible nod in the direction of a couple standing by themselves, isolated by their own invisible barriers. The man was about forty years old, semi-bald, and had heavy bags under his eyes. There was a pigskin suitcase standing beside him. He was easily the most elegant person present, but he was staring into space with vacant, apathetic eyes.

"His papers as an American citizen seem to be okay," Fred told me in a low voice. "He has shown them to all of us, and he has been beefing like hell at all the hardships and privation he had to put up with during the Nazi regime and the war. But somehow he seems to have come through it without spoiling the crease in his pants or getting his collar dirty, and I'd sure like to see what he's got in that there suitcase."

How would the lieutenant act when he caught sight of me? Would he jump at me, or would he just calmly give the guards an order to take me away? Would he ever again be interested in automobile engines and little valves, radiators and jerry cans? And what about my guard? Would he in future use the American words I had taught him as the choicest curses in his vocabulary? Last night. . . . It seemed like an age.

Abbott and Costello lay a hundred years back, Red Eyes a thousand, Carl in Cicerostrasse at least a million and Evald. . . . Strangely enough it only seemed like yesterday that I had said good-bye to Evald. How would he have handled this situation?

"And the dame beside him," Fred continued, indicating an elegant, fur-clad woman nervously shifting her feet and clinging to the arm of the man. "He claims that she's his wife and that the Russians have raped her, which gave her such a shock that she has practically forgotten all her English and now only

310

speaks German." Fred grinned. "But our Russian allies were at least polite enough to let her keep her furs. It'll be interesting, when they start investigating over in our camp, to see what kind of a lady is hiding inside them."

I looked at my watch. My time was up. The next one to open the door might be my lieutenant at the head of a military police squad.

But it wasn't.

When—five minutes later—the door was opened, it admitted some guards and a Russian officer, who told us that the trucks were lined up outside, ready to take us across to the American zone. We filed out through the door in a long line, each receiving a parting nod from the woman behind the desk. When I went past her she suddenly frowned, as if she had just thought of something she had forgotten. Then she let it go, and I got a nod like all the others.

Carefully watched by the armed guards we spread out along the wooden seats on the trucks. A great sigh of relief swept through the crowd, followed by a sudden elation and merriment. Even the airmen started gnawing at their rye loaves in lieu of a parting toast to their hosts. Only the elegant gentleman and his elegant wife, who had lost her English tongue, sat quite still, staring reflectively at the floor boards.

The trucks moved off, drove through the hole in the barbed wire and continued down the drive along the wall. I closed my eyes in a ridiculous attempt to hide myself. My temples seemed about to burst.

"You afraid someone's gonna snatch your Mahorka?" asked the man beside me, another young flier.

I opened my eyes looking down on my package which I had been gripping so hard that my knuckles were white. I relaxed my fingers.

"My father and his father before him have been growing tobacco in Tennessee for God knows how many years," Fred said, to call off the interest of his friend. "When I get home the

311

old man is going to taste this Mahorka. He's always yelling up about young people not having what it takes any more. First of all I'll let him go and vomit, and then I'll tell him that I have smoked at least half a pound of that crap! I guess he'll have to admit that there's still plenty of the old pioneer spirit in the family."

At the head of the pontoon bridge leading across the Elbe, great crowds of Germans had gathered, practically surrounding the trucks.

"Things change quickly these days," Fred said philosophically, and heaved his loaf of rye bread overboard, where it instantly disappeared in a forest of outstretched hands. "Two years ago they were fighting for the whole world. Now they're fighting for a loaf of bread."

At last, when the trucks, with a hollow rumbling and a regular bumping, were well on the bridge, the footbeats that had marched relentlessly through my brain for the past couple of hours faded slowly, until they ceased altogether like feet stopping either because they are too tired to go on, or else because the pursuit is hopeless. And as we went farther across the bridge, and the island appeared, not a mirage but a piece of solid ground, the determined vengeful pursuer changed slowly back into the easygoing and not-too-bright Russian, sitting with eyes half closed on the running board of the little green van, turning his face up at the beam of sunlight slanting through the trees, feeling no enmity towards anybody, just a primitive mind completely open to admit the bright rays of the universe. That was the way I preferred to remember him—and all the Russians I had met like him. The other face of Russia—all the inscrutable, unreliable, brutal, cold fanatics with eyes as hard and unfeeling as the black muzzles of their machine guns—I never wanted to see again. I preferred to forget them completely.

Along the little island's only road, consisting of uneven wheel tracks side by side, a fantastic procession was moving towards us, a vast column of human beings stretching in dense rows across the entire island. It was as if all of Europe's and for that matter all the world's dealers in carnival garments and Hallowe'en gags had got together to create the most grotesque Mardi Gras procession of all times. The great mass of humanity filed past us as an uninterrupted sequence of quaint tableaux. Some pushed baby carriages, rocking precariously on three wheels; others supported themselves on rusty bicycles without tires. Some came with wheelbarrows or children's play carts; one was even dragging a scooter. There were men wearing the grotesquely frivolous pajama-like convict suits of the concentration camps, and clattering along on thin wooden sandals. There were women wearing dented men's hats and men with large cartwheel-brimmed ladies' hats. Men in moldy, green jackets that had been the height of fashion some generations ago, and women in huge buccaneer boots and faded lacy party dresses. Women in their bare feet and men hobbling along with bloodstained linen strips wound around feet and ankles. Some were shaved clean down to the skull, others let their hair fly in the wind. Some carried old lamp-shades, others empty bird cages, and yet others lugged small chests of drawers on their backs.

But eventually as this surrealistic nightmare unfolded before our fascinated eyes, I realized that this was no parade arranged by the carnival dealers. There were bigger if invisible organizers behind it. Hunger and suffering. All curves, all soft lines had been erased from the faces of the paraders. The skin was stretched directly on the hard frame of bones. They were faces carved in wood by some fanatic puritan craftsman. Only the eyes shone brightly in the yellow parchment masks. Eyes with a sharp metallic gleam.

Row after row filed past us, an endless procession, thousands upon thousands. Red was the dominant color. Defiant red. Red rags tied around a tattered sleeve. Red crepe paper streaming from hats. An old, red apron nailed to a stick waving like a banner in the wind. And above the shuffling of countless thousand dragging feet rose a hollow almost inarticulate sound, a monotonous throbbing rhythm, a kind of battle song carried by myriad voices and surging backwards and forwards above the vast columns. The Russians forced into exile were returning home.

The American M.P.'s stood impatiently in all their white painted finery waiting for the procession to pass. But it was not until an hour and a half later that the crowd began to thin out. One of the rear guard was a man in an ancient rain cape and a pair of elastic-sided boots that opened at the toes in a yawning grin every time he took a step. With an ecstatic look in his feverish eyes he was playing away on an old perforated accordion, hoarsely fighting for its breath like a dying man. He was marching along with his head thrown back, lustily singing to his own macabre music.

The American M.P. hitched up his Hopalong Cassidy belt and gave us the sign for departure.

"Singing his way into a fool's paradise," he shouted to me with a grin.

I shrugged my shoulders.

Well—I was out of it now, anyway.